Down Singing River

Down Singing River

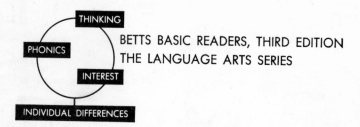

BETTS BASIC READERS, THIRD EDITION
THE LANGUAGE ARTS SERIES

EMMETT A. BETTS

Research Professor in Education and Lecturer in Psychology, School of Education, University of Miami, Coral Gables 46, Florida

CAROLYN M. WELCH

Reading Consultant, Henry S. West Laboratory School, University of Miami, Coral Gables 46, Florida

ILLUSTRATED BY: *James Caraway, Hertha Depper, Dorothea Filosa, William Hutchinson, Jean Michner, Dorothy M. Norman, Maurice Robertson, Bonnie and Bill Rutherford, Thomas L. Sinnickson, Helen Smith, Jane Toan, Irma Wilde*

Cover adapted from art by: *Oscar Liebman*

AMERICAN BOOK COMPANY

New York   Cincinnati   Atlanta   Dallas   Millbrae

3   5   7   9   11   13   15   S.P.   16   14   12   10   8   6   4

STORIES

River People

Old Friends in a River Town

3

Springfield Travelers

Garden City Days

Singing River Secrets

4

River People

A New Home

"Hello, Father," said George,
as Mr. Long walked in the door.
"Did you find us a house by the river?"

"No, I didn't," said Mr. Long. "I have looked
all over town. But I couldn't find one."

"I wish we could live on your boat,"
said George. "That would be fun!"

"Oh, George," laughed Mr. Long.
"People cannot live on work boats."

"I know," said George. "But I like your boat."

"Would you and Betty like to go
for a boat ride?" Mr. Long asked.

"Yes! Yes!" said the children.

"I have to take my boat up the river,"
said Mr. Long. "You can all go with me."

"Good!" said Betty. "And we can look
for a house on the way. Maybe we
will find one in the country."

"I wish we would," said George.

In the morning, the Longs went down
to the river. There they went onto the boat.

Mr. Long took the wheel,
and the ride up the river began.

7

Betty was so happy that she began
to sing. Soon they were all singing.

"It is good to sing on Singing River,"
said Mr. Long.

Mrs. Long had a basket of things to eat.
"Shall we eat on the boat?" she asked.

"Oh, no," said George. "Let us stop
and eat over there!"

George was looking at
a big old house with a big yard.

"We cannot stop in other people's yards,"
said Mr. Long.

"It looks as if no one lives there,"
said Mrs. Long. "Let us stop."

Soon they were off the boat.
They sat down and ate the things
in the basket. Then they ate some candy.

The children went to look at the house.
The paint was old, and the doors were broken.

"I wish we had this house," said George.
"If we did, we could look after it."

Just then they saw a man coming.

"Are you looking at my house?" he asked.

"Oh, is this your house?" asked George.

The man said, "Yes, but I don't
live here. I just came here to fish."

"I wish I could fish," said George.

"And I wish we could live here," Betty said.
"Do you want someone to live in your house?"

"Yes, I do," said the man.

"Come and talk to Father!" said George.

The man went with George and Betty.

"My name is Pine," he said to Mr. Long.
"If you want a country house,
I wish you would look this one over."

"Please do, Father," said George.

10

They all went into the house.

"This house is just right!" said Mrs. Long.

"And my boat will go right by the door," said Mr. Long. "We will take this house."

When the Longs went back to the boat, they were very happy. They talked and talked about their new home.

"We can help get the house ready," said Betty.

"You children have helped," said Mr. Long. "You helped find the house."

George said, "It will be fun to go fishing."

"It will be fun to live by Singing River!" Betty said.

What Do You Think?   Drawing conclusions

Betty's last name is _____.

    White   George   Long

Betty and George take a ride on _____.

    snow   water   road

Betty and George will live by a _____.

    park   spring   river

The Little Toy Boat

One day Betty and her father were talking about Singing River. "Can a river sing?" Betty asked.

"Sometimes it can," her father answered. "Up at White Falls our river sings."

"It does!" said Betty. "I would like to see White Falls."

"We will go in the morning," said Mr. Long. "We can all go."

12

Next day the Longs climbed
into their car.

Betty was holding her toy boat.
It was a good little boat. Betty
liked to play with it in the river.

George was surprised when he saw her
take it into the car.
"I see you have brought your boat,"
he said. "What are you going
to do with it?"

"Oh, I just want to take it along,"
Betty answered.

The road to White Falls went
along the river.

After a time, Betty said, "The river
looks so little here!
It doesn't look like Singing River."

"The river is very little now,"
said Mr. Long.
"But as it comes down from the falls,
brooks and other rivers run into it.
They make it grow into our big river."

"Look at the river now!" said George.
"It is falling over the rocks.
Are we at the falls now?"

Mr. Long answered,
"Yes, this is White Falls."

"The river does sing here," said Betty.
"Singing River is a good name for it here.
Where does all the water come from?"

"Look up there," said Mr. Long.
"Do you see the hills? Rain and
spring water come down from the hills.
They make our river."

15

Mr. Long parked the car.

Then the children ate some cookies that
their mother had brought along.

After that, they climbed on the rocks
by the falls.

"I'm going to sail my boat now,"
Betty said.

"No, don't!" said George.
"It will go over the falls."

But Betty had brought her boat along
to sail. She put it into the water.

Just then the wind came up.
The boat sailed down the river.

"Help!" Betty called to George.

George was too late to help.
The boat was sailing over the falls.

"Oh, my sailboat!" said Betty.

"It will be broken on the rocks," said George.

But Mr. Long said, "It may not be broken. It may sail a long way. This is our river, you know. It runs by our house. Maybe our river will take your boat home."

The Longs went back to the car.
All the way home,
Betty looked for her boat.
But she did not see it.

As soon as they were home, she ran down to the river.

The little boat was not there.

Betty saw an old box on the water.

An apple basket went sailing by.

But there was no little boat.

"What are you doing?" called Mrs. Long.

"I'm looking for my boat!" said Betty.

"Your boat has a long way to come,"
said her father. "Look for it again
in the morning."

Next day Betty stayed by the river.

At last she saw a little red spot.

Then she saw a white sail.

"George!" she called.

"My boat has come back to me!

Our river brought it home."

What Do You Think?   Details

Where did Betty want to go?

Along what river did the Longs ride?

Over what does the river fall?

Where does all the water come from?

What brought Betty's boat home?

18

New Friends

A big yellow bus took Betty and George
to their new school in Green Hills. When school
was over, it took them home again.

One day the Long children brought
two of their new friends home.

"Mother, here are Sue and Jimmy Parker,"
said Betty. "They played in our house
when they were little."

"Yes," said Sue. "We came
to see the family that lived here."

"And now you are coming
to see us!" said Mrs. Long.

"Our dog, Pepper, is coming, too,"
said Jimmy. "But he couldn't come
on the bus."

"No, not on a school bus,"
said Mrs. Long. "How will he get here?"

"In our car," said Sue.
"He will ride along with Father
when he comes to take us home."

"You will like Pepper," said Jimmy.
"He knows all there is to know."

"My! My!" laughed Mrs. Long.
"What a dog! I would like to see
Pepper and all your family."

Then Mrs. Long said, "I know you will
want to play outdoors. And I know
you will want something to eat.
Take this basket of cookies with you."

"Thank you," said the children.

"Where shall we go?" Jimmy asked.
"To the woods," answered Betty.
"There's a big black rock there.
We can eat on it."

"Oh, I know," said Sue.
"We called it the fairy table
when we played here."

They ran into the woods.
There was the big black rock.

21

"Here's the fairy table," Sue said.

"Did you see a fairy here?" George asked.

"Oh, no," laughed Jimmy.

"We just played that a fairy lived here.
That was when we were little."

They sat down and ate their cookies.

"It's fun to eat outdoors," said Betty.
"And this rock makes a good table. I'm going
to put a cookie here for the fairy to eat."

So she put a cookie on the rock.

Then George looked up and said,
"A car is coming up the road."

"That must be our family," said Sue.
"Let us go and see if Pepper has come."

"No," said Jimmy. "Let him find us here
in the woods. Pepper knows
all there is to know."

They sat without talking.
At last Sue jumped up and said,
"Pepper! Here you are!
You did find us! Good dog!"

Pepper ran to the children.

"Here, Pepper," said Jimmy.
"Here's a cookie for you."

But Pepper jumped up on the table
and ate the fairy's cookie!

23

The Talking Fish

There was a man who lived with his wife
in a little house by the river.
The wife worked, and the man fished
all day. But he did not catch many fish.
So they were very, very poor.

Then one day the man did catch
a big fish in the river.

The man was very happy. "What a big fish!"
he said. "At last we will have enough to eat."

Just then the fish began to talk.

"Please let me go," it said. "Oh, fisherman,
put me back into the water and let me live."

"Oh, my!" said the fisherman. "You have said
enough! I don't want to eat a talking fish!"

So he let the fish go.

Back home again, he began
to tell his wife about the fish.

"What did you do with it?" she asked.

"I put it back," the man said.
"What is the use of a talking fish?"

"What is the use!" said the wife.
"Do you not know that a talking fish
can give you what you wish for?
Did you not wish for something?"

"No, I did not," said the fisherman.

"Look at this poor house!" said the wife.
"We do not have enough to eat.
Go back now. Ask the fish
for a good little house with a garden."

26

The man did not want to do so, but
his wife made him go back to the river.

He went to the green water and called,

"Come to me, oh Talking Fish.

Come and give my wife her wish."

Soon the fish came up and asked, "What is it?"

"My wife wants a good little house
with a garden," said the man.

"Go home," said the fish. "She has it now."

The man went back to his wife. Their poor
home had turned into a pretty little house.
It now had a garden, with good things to eat.

So the wife was happy for a time.

Then one day she said, "This house
is too little. I want a big house.
Go to the fish and tell it so."

"No, Wife," said the man. "The fish
will not like that. We have no use
for a big house. This is good enough."

But the wife talked and talked.
At last the poor man went down
to the green water. He called,

"Come to me, oh Talking Fish.

Come and give my wife her wish."

When the fish came up, the man said,
"My wife wants a big house."

"Go home," said the fish. "She has it now."

The man went back to his wife. Their good
little home had turned into a very big house.

"Now, Wife," he said. "This is enough.
I know we shall be happy now."

"We shall see," said the wife.
She was happy for a time.
She had many people to work for her
and a big garden to walk in.

Then one day she said, "This is
not enough. I want to be king!"

"You want to be king!" said the man.
"A woman cannot be king!"

'I WILL be king, and that's that!"
said the wife. "Go back to the fish!"

The poor man went to the river.

It was not green now. It was black,

and a cold rain was falling.

The man called,

"Come to me, oh Talking Fish.

Come and give my wife her wish."

The fish came up.

"What is it now?" it asked.

"My wife wants to be king,"

said the fisherman.

"Go home," said the fish.

"Your wife does not know when she has enough.

You will find her back in your poor old house."

And there they live to this day.

What Do You Think?   Fact and fantasy

Can It Be?

A man can catch a big fish.

A fish can talk to a fisherman.

A wife can wish for many things.

A little house can turn into a big house.

A woman can be a king.

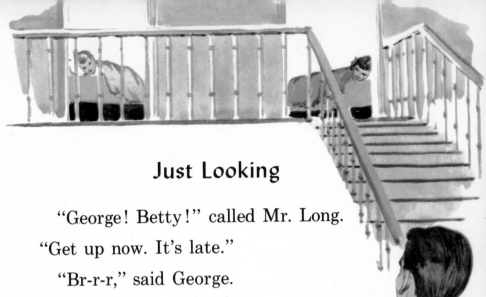

Just Looking

"George! Betty!" called Mr. Long.
"Get up now. It's late."

"Br-r-r," said George.
"I don't want to get up. It's too cold!"

"Yes, it is," said Betty.
"I want to stay where it's warm!"

"You two!" laughed Mr. Long.
"I did want you to help me!"

"What are you doing?" Betty asked.

"I'm not going to tell," said her father.
"Just get up and see."

"All right," said Betty. "I'm coming."

"Not me!" George said as he turned over.
"I'm staying right here!"

31

Betty went to see what her father
was doing. "Oh, you are going to make a fire,"
she said. "That will warm us up."

"Yes," said Mr. Long. "Here, Betty.
Help me with this wood."

As Betty went to help her father,
she looked around the house in surprise.

A little table was overturned.
Many other things were out of place,
and there was broken glass by the door.

"Just look at this house!" she said.
"Did the wind do all this?"

"No, Betty, it wasn't the wind,"
said Mr. Long. "Look around.
Maybe you can find out what it was."

"First, I will put the wood here
by the fireplace," Betty said.

Then she saw something! Far back
in the fireplace sat a big brown and yellow bird.

"Father, what is it?" Betty asked.

"It's a wood duck," said Mr. Long.
"This is what I called you to see."

"Poor little duck," said Betty.
"Are you all right?"

"She's all right," Mr. Long said.
"But our chimney is not the best place
for wood ducks."

"Did she fly down our chimney?" asked Betty.
"Is that how she came into the house?"

"Yes, she was just looking
for a warm place to stay," said Mr. Long.

"So you came to see us last night," Betty said
to the wood duck. "But you didn't like
our house after all, and you couldn't get out."

Just then George came in, too.
"What's going on?" he asked.
"Am I missing something?"

When he saw the wood duck, he said,
"Why didn't you call me?"

"I did," laughed Mr. Long.

"What will we do with the duck?"
George asked.

"We can take her into our woods
by the river," said Mr. Long.

"Poor little duck!" said Betty.
"She wants a place to live, too.
Why don't we make a house just for her?"

"We will," said Mr. Long.
"We will put a box high up on a tree
for her. She will like her tree house.
Then she will stay out of chimneys."

35

Old Father Fish

No other fish was as big
as Old Father Fish.

No other fish had so long
a tail.

No other fish was so old.

"Tell us a story,"
said the little fish. "Tell us
how you came to be so old."

So Old Father Fish would tell
this story.

When I was little,
my mother would say,
    "Play in the river
    When you wish.
    But stay away
    From people who fish."

    One day I saw a fly
in the water.
"That fly looks good enough
to eat," I thought.
    I rolled over on my tail.
I looked again at the fly.
Then I saw a funny old man.
He was fishing with the fly!
    "Oh!" I thought. "My mother
would say to stay away."
    So I did not eat the fly.
I laughed at the man.

37

Then I thought, "I must show
this man how high I can jump."

I jumped and jumped, in and out
of the water. At last I made
a very high jump, right into the boat.
I could not get out!

"This is no place for me," I thought.
"Why, oh why, did I jump so high?"

The funny old man took me home.
He called,

"My good woman,
Come and see.
Here is a fish
For you and me."

38

His funny old wife came out.
She looked at me and said,

"He's not very big,
But he will do.
Yes, he is big enough
For two."

Just then a blackbird came
flying over the funny old house.
When he saw me, he said,

"Why, I was just wishing
That I could go fishing."
Down he came.
He took me by the tail,
and we began to sail up, up, up!
Over the woods and
over the fields we sailed!

39

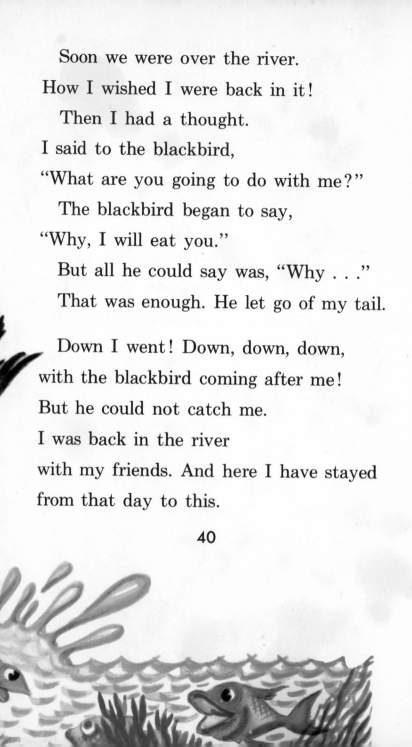

Soon we were over the river.

How I wished I were back in it!

Then I had a thought.

I said to the blackbird,

"What are you going to do with me?"

The blackbird began to say,

"Why, I will eat you."

But all he could say was, "Why . . ."

That was enough. He let go of my tail.

Down I went! Down, down, down,

with the blackbird coming after me!

But he could not catch me.

I was back in the river

with my friends. And here I have stayed

from that day to this.

40

A River Man

Mr. Long's boat was called the Turn About.
It helped to carry things down Singing River.
Then it would turn about and come home.

One morning Mr. Long said to George,
"The Turn About is going out today.
We have to carry some wood to Springfield.
Would you like to go with us?"

"Yes!" said George. "I like to go
to Springfield. And maybe I can help
you and the other men on the boat."

"I don't know about that!"
laughed Mr. Long. "But come along!"

Soon he and George were on the boat.

Three other men worked
on the Turn About. One of them
was called Big John.

"Hello, George," said Big John.
"Do you want to be a river man
like your father?"

"I'm a river man now," said George.

Big John laughed and said,
"You are not big enough."

Then he said, "Are you going to see
your Uncle Ted in Springfield?"

"Yes," said George. "Uncle Ted will
come down to the boat to say hello."

Soon the Turn About was going
down Singing River.

Along the river were woods and fields
and farms.

George saw a boy and a girl
standing by an old red barn.

"Hello, the boat!" they called.

"Hello, the farm!" called George.

"Where are you going?" the boy asked.

"To Springfield," answered George.
"We are carrying wood there."

The Turn About went on down the river

43

After a time George looked up
at the sky. It was growing black,
and the wind was blowing.

"It looks like rain," he said.

Mr. Long, who was at the wheel,
looked at the sky, too.
"Yes, it does," he answered.
"We are going to have a lot of rain."

George and the men put on
their raincoats. Then the rain came.

The boat rocked up and down
as it went through the water.
It rolled this way and that.

44

All the men on the boat had to work.
George worked right along with them.

The boat rolled on through the wind
and the rain. Then it gave a big roll.
As the water ran off the boat,
it took Big John into the cold river!

No one but George saw him fall.
"Help! Help!" called Big John.

"What shall I do?" George thought.
He wanted to call for help, too.
But there was no time.
There was just one thing to do.

"Catch!" George called. "Catch
and hold on!"

45

Soon Big John was climbing
back onto the boat.

The men ran to help him.

"Are you all right?" they asked.

"Yes, I am," said Big John.
"But without George, I would not be
here at all. Now I know he is a river man."

Then Mr. Long said, "A man doesn't
have to be big to be a river man."

"Your uncle will be pleased," Big John
said to George.

"I know what he will say," said George.
"He will say that we have
another river man in the family."

What Do You Think?   Compounds

A town that grows up near a spring
in a field may be called _____.

Fieldhouse   Springfield   Springtime

The coats the men put on in the rain
were _____.

coattails   rainhats   raincoats

46

First Consonant Sounds

brown	brought	rocks

thought	play	place

why	sky	wheel

Last Consonant Sounds

George	along	king

friend	woods	around

last	bus	just

What is it?

Something that turns, first sound of **wh**

Someone to know, last sound of **nd**

Fun to do, first sound of **pl**

Parts of Words: ed

The clown painted his nose.
He put on one coat of paint.

Say **paint** and **painted**. The word **paint**
has one part. How many parts does the
word **painted** have?

Say **painted, lasted,** and **wanted.**
How many parts does each word have?
What is the last letter of **paint**?
Of **last**? Of **want**?

When **ed** is used on a word with the
last letter **t**, you say another part.

Now say **turn** and **turned.**
The word **turn** has one part, and so does
the word **turned.** Say **sail** and **sailed.**
Is there another part when **ed** is used
on **turn** and on **sail**?

What could it be?
A place to live in, painted white
Something sailed down the river

Find Two

1. Things made by man

   boat   sky   table   rock

2. Things a boy can do

   carry   sing   fly   fire

3. People in a family

   wife   why   bus   uncle

4. Boys

   Betty   John   George   field

5. That are water

   rocks   clock   river   brook

6. Things to make you warm

   fire   sail   poor   coat

7. That come from the sky

   field   snow   enough   rain

8. Words that go with **an**

   ate   uncle   answer   men

Sounds You Know	New Words
b in **bus**	
and **all**	ball
l in **lot**	
and **and**	land
m in **must**	
and **et** in **get**	met
f in **fire**	
and **ill** in **will**	fill
l in **late**	
and **ight** in **night**	light
g in **give**	
and **oat** in **boat**	goat
l in **live**	
and **e** in **best**	left
r in **run**	
and **oo** in **soon**	room

Find the New Words

An animal   A toy   Part of a house

Old Friends
in a River Town

The Best Fish

George was staying for a week with Uncle Ted
and Aunt Polly. They lived in Springfield.

Uncle Ted had a fish store.
Each day he brought fish home.

One day George asked,
"Do you catch all the fish we eat?"

"No," laughed Uncle Ted. "I could not catch
so many. Before you go home, I will take
you to see a fishing boat.
Then you will know where I get fish."

One morning George and Uncle Ted
climbed into the truck.

"Get me a good fish," said Aunt Polly.

"I will get you the best fish
of all," said George.

They went through town on the way
to the river. Before long, George
could see the fishing boats.

Uncle Ted took George onto a boat
where men were filling boxes with fish.

"What a lot of fish!" said George.

"Yes," laughed Uncle Ted. "See if you
can find a good one before we leave."

"I will look around," said George.

49

Uncle Ted talked with a fisherman
about the day's catch.

After that, he began to fill his truck
with boxes of fish.

George looked on for a time.
Then he went to find the best fish
of all.

George looked all over the boat.
At the back of the boat he heard
something.

"What is that?" he thought.

Then he heard something again.

"What can that be?" he thought.
"It cannot be a fish. A fish doesn't
make a noise like that."

He looked into one of the boxes.
There was a mother cat with two kittens.
The kittens had made the noise.

As George was playing with a kitten,
a fisherman came along.

"I was looking for a fish," said George.

"That's a funny fish," said the man.
"But you may have it."

"Oh, thank you," said George.

"Are you going to put it on ice?"
the man asked.

"No, this fish doesn't like ice," laughed George.

He put the kitten under his coat
and went to find his uncle.

The truck was filled with fish.

"Ready to go?" asked Uncle Ted.
"Did you find a good fish?"

"The best one of all," answered George.

When they came home, Aunt Polly
asked, "Where is my fish?"

"It's under my coat," said George.

"That's a funny place for a fish,"
said Aunt Polly. "I thought a fish
was put on ice, not under a coat."

Just then they heard a little noise.

"What was that?" asked Aunt Polly.

George took out the kitten.

"Why, that's no fish," said Aunt Polly.

"No, but I thought you would like it,"
said George.

Aunt Polly took the little kitten
in her arms. "I do like it," she said.
"A kitten is just what we want."

"Yes," said Uncle Ted. "Fish will not last,
but a kitten will last a long time."

"A kitten will help you
with the fish, too," said George.

Aunt Polly laughed. "How will
a kitten help with the fish?" she asked.

"Sometimes you may have too many fish,"
said George. "Then the kitten
will help you eat them."

What Do You Think?   Opposites

George was staying with his Uncle Ted
and his _____ Polly.

   Mother   Aunt   Uncle

Uncle Ted talked about fish before he
went to work. He talked about them _____ work, too.

   after   under   along

Uncle Ted asked about a fish, and
George _____ him.

   used   filled   answered

What a Day!

"I wish I had something to do,"
Pat Goodman said to his mother one day.
"Sometimes there isn't a thing to do
in this town! What can I do today?"

"You can take a cookie," his mother
answered. "And then run along."

"Can I help you?" Pat asked.

"No, thank you," said Mrs. Goodman.
"I don't want you in the kitchen now."

"You look as if you know something
I don't know," said Pat.

His mother laughed. "Just run along
outdoors and play," she said.

"I wish George Long were here,"
Pat said. "We had fun when he
lived here in Springfield."

"Why, Pat, you have a lot
of other friends," Mrs. Goodman said.

"Yes," said Pat. "But I miss George.
I haven't seen him for a long time."

Then he went out of the kitchen
and walked down the street with his dog.

Before long, he saw his friend Jack.
"Hello, Jack," he said. "Let's play."

"I don't want to play right now,"
said Jack.

"That's funny," thought Pat,
as Jack went on down the street.
"I have never seen him
when he didn't want to play."

Pat walked on.

Soon he met the Brooks twins.
"Hello," he said. "Let's go
to the field and play."

"We cannot play today,"
said the twins. "We have on
our best things."

"Why do you wear your best things
today?" asked Pat.

"We cannot tell you,"
the twins laughed.

"That's funny," thought Pat.
"I have never seen a thing
like this before."
He called to his dog,
and they walked on.

Next Pat met Penny Barns.

She was wearing her best clothes, too.

"Will you play with me
and my dog?" asked Pat.

"No," said Penny. "I'm wearing
my best clothes. Don't you know
what is going on today?"

"No," said Pat. "I haven't heard.
What is going on?"

But Penny would not tell.

Pat went on. Soon he met
three other friends. They were all
wearing their best clothes.
Not one of them would play.

"This is very funny," Pat thought.

"I have seen a lot of my friends. They are all wearing their best clothes. They look as if they are going to a party."

But Pat's friends would never have a party without asking him.

He hadn't heard about a party.

So he went on with his dog to the field.

Pat liked to play outdoors, but today he did not have fun.

"Let's go home," he said to his dog.

As Pat went in through the kitchen door, he called, "Mother, I'm home."

Then Pat heard a noise. People were laughing.

Why, there were all the children he had met!

"See who is here!" they called.

There was George Long!

"George!" said Pat. "You came back!"

"Yes," said George. "I wanted to surprise you."

"We wanted to surprise you, too," said Jack.

"That's why we didn't tell you about the party."

So it was a party after all!

"I never had a surprise

like this before," said Pat.

59

A New Boat for Springfield

Pat and his friend Jack liked to go down to the river to see the boats.

There were big boats and little boats. There were work boats and fishing boats. There were boats for people who wanted to ride up and down the river.

One day the boys heard some of the boatmen talking.

"We have so many boats," said one man. "Some day a boat may catch fire. I wish we had a fireboat."

Pat said to the boatman, "I have never seen a fireboat. What does it do?"

The man answered, "You know how
a fire truck puts out fires on land.
A fireboat puts out fires on water."

"Do many towns have them?" asked Jack.

"Not many," said the man.
"Fairwater has a fireboat."

"I wish our town would buy one," said Pat.

Soon many people were talking
about a fireboat. The boatmen wanted one.
But the men who had stores did not.

"Why do we want a fireboat?" the men
in the stores asked. "A fireboat would be
of no use to us. It couldn't put out fires on land."

One day the boatmen said,
"Let's put on a show.
We can ask the men from Fairwater
to show their fireboat to our town.
Then our people may want one, too."

So the fireboat came to Springfield.
People from all over town went down
to the river to see the show.

The river firemen showed how
their boat worked. All the people
looked at it from the land.

The people of Springfield said, "That was
a good show." But then they began to leave.

Soon many people had left, but
Jack and Pat stayed to see all they could.

One of the firemen saw them and called,
"Would you boys like to look around our boat?"

"Yes!" answered Jack. "We have never
been on a fireboat."

So the boys went on the boat, and
the fireman showed them around.

"Where do you get the water
to put out fires?" asked Pat.

"We get it from the river," said the fireman.

After the boys had seen all the things
on the boat, they looked out at the town.
To their right and left, they could see
stores and many other buildings on land.

Jack was looking at a little store
not far from the water. "Pat!" he said.
"Look at that building!"

Then he called out, "Fire! Fire!"

The people on land could not see the fire.
But it could be seen from the water.

The fireboat men began to work fast.
Soon river water was falling on the fire.

Then people began to run.

"The fire truck is coming!" they called.

Before the truck could get there,
the fire had been put out.

The people called to the firemen,
"Good for you! If it had not been
for you, there would be no store left!"

"Thank the boys," said the men.
"They saw the fire from the boat."

"We don't want thanks," said the boys.
"We want Springfield to have a fireboat."

"The boys are right," said the people.
"Our town has many boats. We have
many buildings by the water. We can
use a fireboat in Springfield."

What Do You Think?   Definite terms

How many boys go down to the river?
How many fireboats does Fairwater have?
How many buildings are on fire?
How many fireboats can Springfield use?

The Horse That Liked Ice Cream

Whitey was an old horse who
worked in the park.

He gave the children rides
on his back. The children liked him.

"Go on, old Whitey," they said.
And around and around he went.

He was not very big. He did not run fast.
So he was a good, safe horse to ride.

One day it was very warm, and many children
wanted to ride. Whitey wanted something
to eat, but there was no time to stop.

Whitey was not just a safe horse.
He was clever, too. He thought
of a way to get something to eat.

Whitey turned his head around and
saw a boy who was eating ice cream.

"That looks good," thought Whitey.

Before the boy could stop him,
Whitey ate the ice cream.

"Oh!" called the boy.
"Whitey ate all my ice cream!
There's nothing left!"

67

The Park Man looked surprised. He had
never heard of a horse that ate ice cream.

"No, no, Whitey!" he said.
"You must not do that."

Whitey said nothing. But he thought,
"That was clever! I must do that again."

Whitey went on working. After a time,
he saw another boy who was eating ice cream.
Before the Park Man could stop him,
Whitey ate it, too.

After that, Whitey wanted
ice cream all the time.

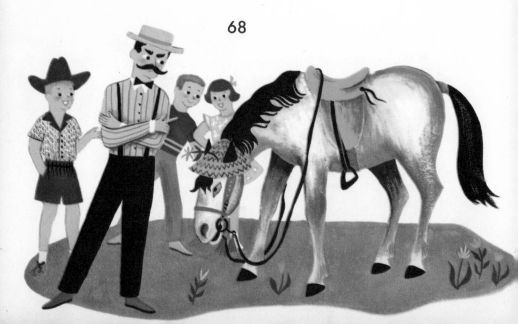

Day after day, clever Whitey took
ice cream away from the children.
The Park Man could do nothing to stop him.

Then one very warm day a man came
through the park with a wagon.
On the wagon was painted

ICE CREAM

"Who wants ice cream?" called the man.
The children ran to buy some.

Whitey was happy. "Now I will get
lots of ice cream," he thought.

He turned to take some.
But the Park Man had had enough.

"Whitey," he said. "You cannot work here.
You are a good, safe horse. But no children
will want rides if you take their ice cream."

The Ice Cream Man heard this.
He pulled his wagon over to the Park Man.

"I will buy your horse," he said. "He can pull
my wagon for me. I have pulled it long enough."

So now clever Whitey works
for the Ice Cream Man. He sees
the children each day in the park.
He gets all the ice cream he wants.

70

A Funny Day

A bear climbed into an airplane
  And soon was sailing high.
A dog went down a chimney,
  I cannot tell you why.

An old hen ran to a circus.
  A horse put on a hat.
He did look very funny,
  I have to tell you that.

A monkey danced on a pumpkin.
  A kitten and a duck
Took many little rabbits
  And traveled on a truck.

An old pig put a coat on,
  So the story goes,
And traveled through the country
  With an apple on his nose!

Spot

Spot was a big white dog
with many black spots and a long tail.
He lived with the Hill family.

In the Hill family there were
two little girls. One was called May,
and her little sister was named Sue.

The sisters were happy with Spot.
He pulled their little wagon
and played games with them.

Then one day twins came to live
next door. They had a pretty little dog
that could hold a ball on his nose.

When the sisters saw this clever dog,
they were not happy with Spot.

May said, "Spot is the best dog
in Springfield. But he is big and
funny-looking! I wish he were clever
and could hold a ball on his nose."

"Maybe we can train him
to do that," said Sue.

So the sisters worked and worked
with Spot, but they could not train him.

Then Sue said, "If we cannot train him,
maybe we can make him pretty."

"But what can we do?" said May.
"We cannot change him."

"Maybe I can change his spots,"
thought Sue.

One day when May was at school,
Sue took out a box of paints.
She put red and yellow and blue paint
all over the dog's black spots.

"I changed you, Spot," she said.

When May came home, she said,
"Oh, Sue, what did you do?
You made Spot look like a clown!"

For a long time the painted spots
would not wear off. But at last
they did.

Then one day a man came to town.
He gave magic shows
in the school building. May and Sue
went to one of his shows.

The man had a big black box.

"This is a magic box," he said.

"It can change things. Do you have
something you would like to change?"

One boy handed a schoolbook
to the Magic Man. The man put
the book into the box. Then he took out
a ball and a bat!

May said to the Magic Man,
"Did you ever change a dog?
Could you change our funny-looking Spot
into a pretty little dog?
One that can hold a ball
on his nose?"

"Go and get your dog," said the man.
"I will change him."

"Will it hurt him?" asked Sue.

"No, it will not hurt him," said the man.

The girls ran home for Spot.

They took him to the Magic Man.

He said to Spot, "Come on, now!
Jump into the box. You will be safe.
.I will not hurt you."

Spot jumped in.

Then the man did some funny things
with his hands.

He said some magic talk.

Out jumped a pretty little dog!

"Thank you," said Sue. "This is
the best dog we have ever seen."

"Can he hold a ball on his nose?"
asked May.

"Yes," said the man. "He can."

The girls took the dog home,
but he would not play with them.
He was no fun at all!

"Spot was not pretty and clever,"
said May. "But he was fun!"

"I wish we had Spot back," said Sue.

So they went to the Magic Man again.

"Please change this little dog,"
said May. "Give us back our Spot."

"Jump into the box, little dog,"
the man said. "I will not hurt you."

He worked his magic again.

Out of the box jumped Spot!

"Oh, Spot!" said May. "Good old
funny-looking Spot! Come home with us,
and stay the way you are forever!"

What Do You Think? Analysis of sentences

The man put the book into the box.
    Who did something?   What did he do?
The girls ran home for Spot.
    Who did something?   What did they do?

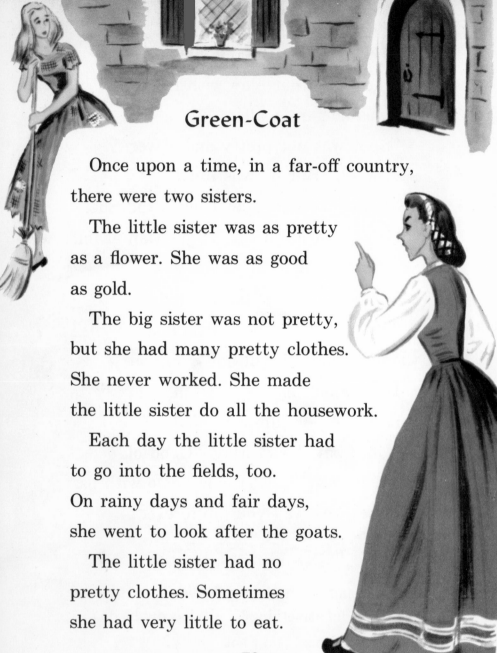

Green-Coat

Once upon a time, in a far-off country, there were two sisters.

The little sister was as pretty as a flower. She was as good as gold.

The big sister was not pretty, but she had many pretty clothes. She never worked. She made the little sister do all the housework.

Each day the little sister had to go into the fields, too. On rainy days and fair days, she went to look after the goats.

The little sister had no pretty clothes. Sometimes she had very little to eat.

Once the little sister was
out in the fields with the goats.
"I can drink water from the brook,"
she said. "But I cannot eat leaves
as the goats do. I wish I had
something to eat!"

At this, a little white goat said,
"I will help you. Come along."

The girl was surprised.
But she followed the goat
through the woods to a little house.

"Go in," said the goat.
"Eat and drink whatever you like."

The girl did so. Then she
followed the goat back to the field.

Each day the goat took the girl
to the little house in the woods.
There, in a pretty little room,
she had all she wanted to eat and drink.

She began to grow very pretty.

"Someone must be feeding her,"
the big sister thought. "I must
find out at once who it is!"

So she followed the girl to the fields.
She saw the goat talk to the girl
and take her to the little house.
She looked into the room and saw
the little sister eating.

When the girl came home,
the sister said, "Your goat is magic.
I will take him away at once."

"Oh, no! Please do not!" said the girl.
She did not know what to do.

That night the magic goat said,
"I will carry you to a safe place.
Jump upon my back."

The girl did so, and the goat took
her away. He ran until they were
safe, far away in the green woods.

The night was windy,
and the poor girl was cold.
So the goat made her a warm coat
out of green leaves.

Then they traveled on
until they came to a big house.

"There is the king's house,"
said the goat. "Go in and ask
for work."

81

The girl went to the kitchen.

"Who are you?" asked a woman.

"You may call me Green-Coat,"
said the girl. "I am looking for work."

"You may work in the kitchen,"
said the woman. "The king is going
to have a party. There is work to do."

"Is there room for my little goat?"
asked Green-Coat.

"Yes, there is room in the barn,"
the woman answered.

So the girl helped in the kitchen,
and the goat ate leaves in the field.

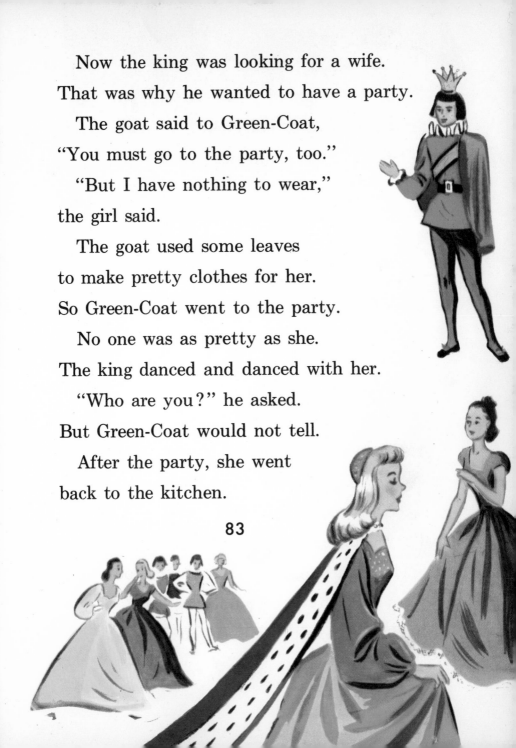

Now the king was looking for a wife.
That was why he wanted to have a party.

The goat said to Green-Coat,
"You must go to the party, too."

"But I have nothing to wear,"
the girl said.

The goat used some leaves
to make pretty clothes for her.
So Green-Coat went to the party.

No one was as pretty as she.
The king danced and danced with her.

"Who are you?" he asked.
But Green-Coat would not tell.

After the party, she went
back to the kitchen.

83

The king wanted to see Green-Coat
again. He looked and looked for her,
but he could not find her.

One day in the garden, he saw
a white goat eating leaves.

"Oh, King," said the goat.
"The girl you are looking for
is in your kitchen."

When he heard this, the king was happy,
and he ran at once to the kitchen.
There was Green-Coat.

The king took Green-Coat by the hand.
"Will you be my wife?" he asked.

"Yes," said Green-Coat. "I will,
if my white goat may stay with me."

The king laughed. "I will build your goat
the best barn in the land," he said.
"Did he not help me find you?"

Halloween on the River

It was George Long's last day in Springfield.
He and Pat Goodman sat on the fence talking.

"I wish I didn't have to go,"
said George. "I have had a good time."

"Tonight you will have the best time
of all," said Pat with a smile.

"Why?" George asked his friend.

"It's Halloween," said Pat.

"I know it is," said George.
"But what are we going to do?"

"Wait and see," said Pat, and he
smiled again. "You will say Halloween
is the best night of the year."

That evening George asked Uncle Ted
about Halloween in Springfield.
"It's windy tonight, just right
for Halloween," he said.
"But why is it the best evening
of the year?"

"Wait and see," said Uncle Ted.

Soon George heard noises
in the street. He ran out-of-doors.

Coming down the street was a parade
of people, big and little. There were
Pat and all his friends.

"Come with us, George!" Pat called.

"May I go?" asked George.

"Yes," said Uncle Ted with a smile.
"Go along. I will follow you soon."

So George went down the street
with the others.

"Pat!" said George. "If we go
this way, we will come to the river!"

"That's right," said Pat.

"What are we going to do by the river
this evening?" asked George.

"Just wait until we get there,"
said Pat. "Then you will see."

When they came to the river,
they walked onto a houseboat.
Yellow pumpkins were placed here
and there on the boat. Each pumpkin
had a light in it.

"A party on a houseboat!" said George.
"What a surprise!"

"We had a party here
last Halloween, too," said Pat.

The children went into a big room
lighted with Halloween pumpkins.
Black cats and bats were painted
all around the room.

Just then a voice called, "Who-o-o!"
All the lights went out.

"Oh!" said the children. "What's that?"

Someone in white walked into the room.
"I am the voice of the river," he said.

Then the lights went on.

"Uncle Ted!" said George.
"I didn't know you!"

Uncle Ted laughed. "Halloween is a time
for surprises," he said. "Now let's all
play games! First we will duck
for apples. Someone will get a prize."

George thought he could get
the prize. He was good at this game.

Then he looked at his friend Pat.
He could see that Pat wanted to get
the prize, too.

"I will not see Pat again
for a long time," George thought.
"I will let him get the prize."

So when it was George's turn,
he let the apples get away from him.

Then it was Pat's turn. Down went his head.
Up he came with an apple!

"Pat gets the prize," said Uncle Ted.

He gave Pat an airplane.

Then the mothers came in

with pumpkin pies and ice cream.

As the children took their places

at the table, George went over to Pat.

"That's a good airplane," he said.

"You were good at ducking for apples."

All too soon it was time to go.

On the way home, Uncle Ted talked

with George in a pleased voice.

"You know something, George," he said.

"You are a pretty good friend."

George smiled. Pat had been right.

This night was the best of all.

What Do You Think?   Drawing conclusions

The game of ducking for apples was played
at a Halloween _____.

    story   play   party

The prize was something to _____.

    drink   fly   wear

Study Pages

Sounds of ch and tch

You know the sound of **ch** in **children**.

The letters **ch** are consonant letters.

The sound of **ch** is in the word **catch**.

Three consonant letters, **tch**, stand

for the sound of **ch** in **catch**.

What letters stand for the sound

of **ch** in **chimney**, **each**, **change**, **kitchen**?

What is part of a fireplace? Part of a house?

One Sound of th

You know the sound of **th** in **their**.

This sound is a consonant sound.

The letters **th** are consonant letters.

Say the words and find two that

rhyme: **they**, **there**, **other**, **mother**, **then**.

Does the word **there** tell "where" or "who"?

Does the word **then** tell "time" or "place"?

Sound of the Vowel a in at

You know the sound of **a** in **at**, **an**, and **glass**. Say the sound.

Now say the words **landing**, **magic**, and **travel**. How many parts does each word have? Say the first part of each word. Say the sound of the vowel in the first part of each word.

Have you seen? a cat in a glass hat

an airplane landing

Sound of the Vowel i in it

You know the sound of **i** in **it**, **big**, and **sing**. Say the sound.

Say the words **river**, **sister**, and **filling**. Say the first part of each word. Say the sound of the vowel in the first part of each word.

Have you seen? a river of cream

a boy's sister

Thoughts About Friends

If you want to make a new friend,
smile and say something to him.

What is one of the best ways to make
a new friend?

When a friend has a lot of books
to carry, ask to carry some of them.

When do you ask to carry
a friend's books?

To be a good friend, take turns
in playing games with others.

What is one way to be a friend?

When two friends get a drink of water,
one of them waits for the other.

When does a friend wait?

A friend is someone who likes to help
you with your work.

Who is a friend?

Sounds You Know	New Words
ar in **arm**	bark
oo in **took**	foot
ee in **seen**	need, keep
a in **bag**	sad
ea in **eat**	read
i in **fish**	milk, sit
sh in **shall**	
and **ould** in **could**	should
fl in **fly**	
and **oor** in **door**	floor
st in **stay**	
and **ood** in **wood**	stood

Find in the New Words

The sound a dog makes

Something children drink

What you do with a book

One of your two feet

Springfield Travelers

SEE
GARDEN
CITY
by Bus
25¢

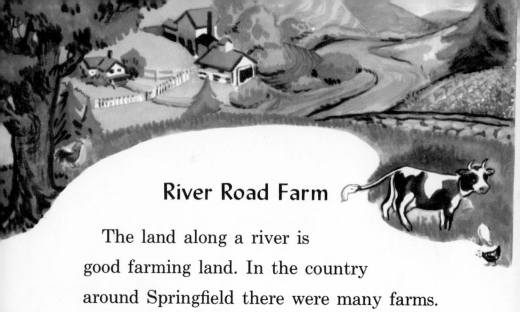

River Road Farm

The land along a river is
good farming land. In the country
around Springfield there were many farms.

One of the best was River Road Farm,
where Mr. and Mrs. Brown lived.

Springfield people liked Mr. Brown.
They said he was a good farmer.
They said his apples and his corn
were the best they could buy.

The Hill family liked Mr. Brown's farm
and the good things they could buy there.
May and Sue Hill liked the farmer, too.
Every time they went to the farm,
he had something new to show them.

92

One day the Hills were going
to River Road Farm.

Spot, their dog, ran to the car.

But Mrs. Hill said,
"No, Spot. You must stay at home.
Every time we take you,
you bark at the hens."

"Oh, let's take him," said Sue.
"Maybe this time he will be good."

"No," said her mother.
"If he does not bark at the hens,
he will bark at something.
When we take Spot away from home,
he does nothing but bark!"

Mrs. Hill put a big basket
into the back of the car.
"This will hold everything
we buy at the farm," she said.

Soon the Hills were on the River Road.
From the car they could watch the boats
coming down the river.

"The sailboats look like birds,"
said Sue.

"Yes," said May. "Spot would like
to watch them. Poor Spot!
He had to stay home."

Just then there was a funny noise
from the back of the car.

"What can that be?" May asked.

Sue turned around. There was
a dog's foot showing under the basket.

"Oh!" said Sue.

"What is it?" asked Mrs. Hill.
But May and Sue said nothing.

The car turned into the farmyard.

"Oh, look!" said May. "There are four baby goats. Spot would like them!"

At this, there was another noise from the back of the car.

May turned around and saw another foot under the basket. She laughed.

"What is going on?" her mother asked. Again the girls said nothing.

Then Mr. Brown came to help them out of the car. His dog, Watch, came with him.

Watch went to the car and barked.

There was a bark from the car. Out jumped Spot on all four feet!

"Oh, Spot!" said Mrs. Hill.

"How did you get here?"

Spot just barked again.

"Stop that, Spot!" said May.

But Mr. Brown said, "Today he may bark.
We have something for him to bark at."

"What is it?" asked the children.

"A woodchuck," the farmer said.
"For days he has been eating my corn.
Watch cannot catch him. Maybe Spot can help."

Then Mr. Brown said to the dogs,
"Get the woodchuck, boys!"

Off ran the dogs, and the Hills went
to the house for a drink of water.

Soon they heard the dogs barking
and barking. They all ran out
to see what was going on.

The dogs had run the woodchuck
into a basket! He was not hurt,
but he could not get away.

"Good dogs!" said Mr. Brown,
as he gave them each a pat.

"It's a good thing Spot came,"
he said to the girls. "He helped
catch the woodchuck."

Then the farmer brought an old bag
and put it over the basket.

"Now what shall we do
with Mr. Woodchuck?" he asked.

"Could we take him home?" Sue asked.

But Mrs. Hill said, "Oh, no.
A woodchuck couldn't live in a house."

"If we let him go, he will eat
the corn again," said May.

"I know what to do," said Sue.
"We can take him to the park!"

"That's right," said Mrs. Hill.
"With a fence around him, he cannot
hurt people's gardens."

So when the Hills went back to town,
Mr. Woodchuck went, too. Spot barked,
but it was all right.

After all, Spot had helped catch
Mr. Woodchuck. He had
a right to bark!

1   2   3

A woodchuck went to live in a park.

Two dogs ran a woodchuck into a basket.

An animal surprised the Hills.

Lightfoot

Once upon a time there was
a little pig who could run very fast.
So she was called Lightfoot.

There were other pigs
on Farmer Ball's farm.
But Lightfoot was the only one
who did not want to be a pig.

"Pigs only eat," she said.
"I can do other things."
And she could.

Lightfoot ran all over the farm and
made friends with the other animals.
She learned to talk like them.

She watched the farmer every day.
She learned how to do all the work
on the farm.

Farmer Ball was not pleased. "I am
the farmer here," he said to Mrs. Ball.
"Lightfoot should learn to be a pig."

Mrs. Ball only smiled. She thought
Lightfoot was very clever.

Lightfoot went on learning.
She learned how the watchdog should bark.
She learned how the hens should look
after eggs. She learned how the horses
should get in hay.

But she did not learn to be a pig.

People came from all over to see Lightfoot.

"They stand around and look at her as if
she were in a circus," Farmer Ball said.
"I don't want a circus on my farm.
I have a lot of work to do."

"A circus is fun," said Mrs. Ball.

One night Farmer Ball went to the barn
to get the milk.

Lightfoot ran along to help with the milking.
This did not please Farmer Ball.

He said to Mrs. Ball, "I don't need
a pig to help with the milking.
Lightfoot should be in a circus.
Let us go to town and ask
the Circus Man if he wants her."

101

Next morning Farmer and Mrs. Ball
climbed into their wagon. They went
to town and saw the Circus Man.

"My!" said the Circus Man. "A pig like yours
should be in the circus. I will buy Lightfoot."

Farmer Ball said, "Come to the farm.
You may take her and keep her."

Before they could get ready,
the sky turned black. The wind
began to blow. The rain began to fall.

The rain filled the river, and
the river ran over the road.

Farmer and Mrs. Ball and
the Circus Man could not leave town.

Farmer Ball was very sad.

"I must get back to the farm," he said.

"I must see to things at home."

"It's no use being sad," said the Circus Man.

"Come to my circus until the rain is over."

So they went to the circus.

Farmer Ball could not stop being sad,

but Mrs. Ball had a good time.

Now it was raining at the farm, too.

The animals said to each other,

"It looks as if Farmer Ball is not coming.

We don't need to keep on working."

So the hens would not look after

their eggs. The horses would not get

the hay in. The dog would not bark.

Lightfoot said, "This is not fair.
We must all help with the farm work."
She made each animal get to work.

Next morning Farmer Ball came home
with Mrs. Ball and the Circus Man.

What a surprise they had! The hay was
in the barn. The milk was in the cans.
The eggs were in the baskets.

"Who did this?" Farmer Ball asked.

"How can you ask?" said Mrs. Ball.
"Lightfoot showed the animals what to do."

The Circus Man could not wait to buy
Lightfoot for his circus.

But Farmer Ball said, "Lightfoot
is too good for the circus. She is
our helper and our friend. I know it now
I need her here on the farm.
I will keep her after all."

Pat and Joe Go Traveling

This was the day Pat and Joe Goodman had been waiting for.

They were going to Garden City.

They were going on a boat called the River Girl.

No one was going with them.

For the very first time, they would travel alone!

"Pat, can you look after Joe?" Mrs. Goodman asked.

"Oh, yes," said Pat. "Father will put us on the boat. Uncle Jack will come to get us in Garden City. We will have fun."

"I don't know that you're old enough
to travel alone," said Mrs. Goodman.

"We are! We are!" said Joe. "We're not
too young! We can go alone!"

His mother smiled. "Then come and eat
something before you get ready," she said.

"I want a piece of pie," said Pat.

"Milk and eggs first!" his mother said.

Mr. Goodman took the boys
to the boat landing. There they met
Mr. Downs, who ran the boat.

"Good morning," said Mr. Goodman.
"Here are my two boys, Pat and Joe.
They're going alone to Garden City."

Mr. Downs said, "Boys, you came
on the right day. I have a young helper
who will look after you. Wait here,
and he will be along soon."

"Have a good time, boys,"
said Mr. Goodman as he left the boat.

Mr. Downs went to the wheelhouse.
Soon the River Girl was on her way.

Pat looked for Mr. Downs's helper,
but he did not see him.

Just then a red-headed boy ran up
to Pat. He handed Pat a piece
of paper and then ran away.

Pat looked at the piece of paper.
It said

NO EMOC

Pat looked at the paper again,
but he couldn't read what it said.

107

The red-headed boy came back
and gave Pat another piece of paper.

This time the paper said

EM WOLLOF

Again Pat could not read it.

"Wait here," he said to Joe. "I will
go look for Mr. Downs's helper."

Pat went all around the boat.
He saw no one who looked
like a boatman's helper.
And he did not see
the red-headed boy again.

So he went back to find Joe. But Joe
was not where Pat had left him.

Pat did not know what to do.

He just had to find Joe!

As he turned around, he saw
the red-headed boy watching him.
Then the boy smiled and ran
up to the wheelhouse.

"I'm not going to let him get away this time,"
thought Pat. "Maybe he knows where Joe is."

So Pat followed the red-headed boy
into the wheelhouse. There was Mr. Downs
at the wheel. And there was Joe!

"Joe!" said Pat. "Here you are!"

"Yes," laughed Joe.
"Mr. Downs's helper brought me."
And he looked at the red-headed boy.

Mr. Downs laughed, too.

"This is my boy, Sonny," he said.

"He is my young helper."

"Why did he give me the pieces
of paper?" Pat asked.

"Sonny likes to play games," said Mr. Downs.
"You have to know how to read Sonny's papers."

"You must read the last letter first,"
said Sonny.

Pat looked at the pieces of paper.
The first one said

NO EMOC

"Oh!" said Pat. "Let me see.

COME ON

Why, I can read it now."

110

On the next paper was

EM WOLLOF

Pat said, "I can read this one, too.

FOLLOW ME

And I did follow you, Sonny."

Everyone laughed.

"I like this game," said Pat.

"It's fun to play, if you know how."

"This boat ride is fun, too," said Joe.

"Do we have to get off soon?"

"No," said Mr. Downs.

"It's a long way to Garden City.

You have lots of time for fun."

So the three boys played on the boat

until they came to the city.

There Uncle Jack met the boat.

"Here we are!" said Joe.

"We traveled alone."

What Do You Think?   Following directions

Read from right to left.

.NUF EB NAC ENOLA GNILEVART

Joe Makes a Call

"Here we are, Pat and Joe,"
said Uncle Jack. "This is where I live."

The boys looked up at a high building
with many floors. They saw letter boxes
by the door. One box said

MR. AND MRS. J. GOODMAN

"I know who they are!" said Joe.
Another box said

MR. AND MRS. L. TURNER

Another box said

MRS. A. B. BIRD

"Mrs. Bird!" said Joe.
"She should know how to fly!"

"What a lot of neighbors you have!"
said Pat. "Do you know them all?"

"In the city we don't know
all our neighbors," said Uncle Jack.
"Some people want to be left alone."

"That's funny!" said Joe.

Uncle Jack took Pat and Joe
into the elevator.

"Hello, boys," said the elevator man.

"Hello," said Pat. "I have never been
in an elevator before."

"Hold on, then," laughed the man.

The elevator went up to the top floor,
where the boys saw four doors. One had
the name MRS. A. B. BIRD on it.

"Mrs. Bird lives on the top floor!"
said Joe. "Do you know her, Uncle Jack?"

"No," said Uncle Jack. "Mrs. Bird is
one who wants to be alone. She never
talks to the other people in the house.
But here is someone who wants to talk."

He opened a door. There was the boys' aunt.

"Hello, boys," she said. "I am
so happy to see you!"

Two young neighbors were there.

"Here are Mary and Dick Turner,"
said Mrs. Goodman. "They came to say hello."

"Hello," said Pat. "We saw the name
Turner on one of the letter boxes."

"We live on this floor, too," said Mary.

"Where do you play?" asked Joe.

"Down in the play yard," said Dick.

Every day the four children went down
to the play yard. Sometimes they went up
and played on the roof of the building.
Soon they were the best of friends.

Mary and Dick took Pat and Joe
to the other neighbors' homes. Soon
the boys had met everyone but Mrs. Bird.

"Why don't we go there?" asked Joe.
"I want to see if she can fly."

"People don't fly," laughed Mary. "And
Mrs. Bird doesn't want to see people."

"Maybe we should make a call on her,"
said Joe. "That's what we do at home."

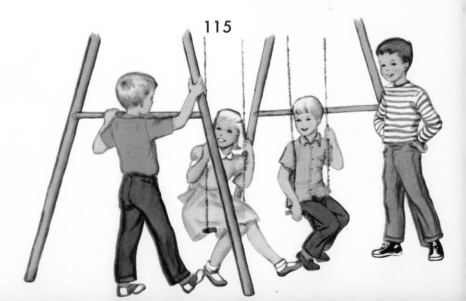

One day when Mary and Dick came
to the Goodmans' home, Joe was not there.

"I don't know where he went," said Pat.
"We must look for him."

The children went down in the elevator.
They asked the elevator man if he
had seen Joe, but he had not.
They looked in the play yard. They went up
and looked on the roof. They asked
the neighbors on Uncle Jack's floor.

No one had seen Joe.

Pat said, "Mrs. Bird is the only one
we have not asked."

"I don't want to ask her," said Mary.
"She doesn't talk to people."

"But I must find Joe," said Pat.
"If you're not coming, I will go alone."

"We will come, too," said Dick.

Mrs. Bird's door was open.

"Are you home?" Pat called.

"Come in," a voice answered.

The three children walked in.
There was a happy-looking woman. And there
was Joe on the floor, looking at an open book.

"Why, Joe!" said Mary. "We have looked
for you from the yard to the roof!"

"I came to see Mrs. Bird," said Joe.

Mrs. Bird said, "I have been here
four weeks. Joe is my first caller."

"You see?" said Joe. "She likes to talk
to people who come to see her.
But she cannot fly!"

A Runaway Bus

Uncle Jack's work was to drive
a bus. Pat and Joe liked to ride
with him all over the city.

One night Joe said, "We had a good time
today, Uncle Jack. It was fun to ride
on a big new bus like yours."

"All the buses in Garden City
are big and new," said Uncle Jack.

"Why is that?" asked Pat.

"It's all Uncle Freddie's doing,"
said Uncle Jack.

"Who is Uncle Freddie?" asked Pat.

"Tell us what happened," said Joe.

"This is the story," said Uncle Jack.

Two boys, Dick and John, came
to the city. They came to see
their Uncle Freddie, who was a busman.

Uncle Freddie's bus was an old bus
that ran on the back streets of town.
Only new buses ran on the best streets.

Now Uncle Freddie wanted to show
the best streets to Dick and John.
He wanted to show them the best stores.
Then, too, he just wanted a change!

Uncle Freddie met the boys at the train.
"Get in the bus, boys," he said.
"I want to show you the town."

Uncle Freddie turned to the other people
in the bus. "This bus is going
to Kingman Street," he told them.
"Please get off and take the next bus."

The people did as they were told.
But one old man would not get off.

"A little old bus like this should not
run on Kingman Street," said the man.
"This happens to be a Rock Street bus.
It should stay on Rock Street."

"I want to drive on Kingman Street just once,"
said Uncle Freddie. "Sometimes a busman
needs a change. Will you please get off?"

"No, I will not!" said the old man.
"I shall sit right here."

"Sit there if you wish,"
said Uncle Freddie. "You will go where
we go. You will ride on Kingman Street
with Dick and John and me."

The boys had a wonderful time.

"That is the Kingman Building,"
Uncle Freddie told them. "Over there is
Kingman Park. There is the Kingman Store."

At last Dick asked, "How does it
happen that everything is named Kingman?"

Uncle Freddie said, "Old Mr. Kingman
does many good things for our city.
He gave us this wonderful park.
He puts up buildings and stores.
All the buses are his."

"Then why do you drive
this old brown bus?" John asked.
"Mr. Kingman should give you
a new bus."

"A big green one!" said Dick.

Uncle Freddie looked sad.

"I wish I could have a new green bus,"
he said. "I don't know why Mr. Kingman
keeps this old bus on the streets."

"Maybe he would give you a new one
if you asked him," said John.

Just then the old man called out
from the back of the bus.
"Stop this runaway bus!" he said.
"All of you must come with me."

They all did as they were told.
They followed the man to a big house.

The door was opened by the housekeeper.
"Good evening, Mr. Kingman," she said.

"Mr. Kingman!" said Uncle Freddie.

Then the old man smiled.

"Yes, I am Mr. Kingman," he said.

"I thought you would be surprised."

Uncle Freddie didn't know what to say!

"Come in and sit down,"
said Mr. Kingman. "Let's have something
to eat. You must all stay for supper."

"We would like to," said the boys.

After supper Mr. Kingman said,
"I didn't know that busmen liked a change."

"Everyone does," said Uncle Freddie.

"Then everyone shall have a change,"
said Mr. Kingman. "Garden City shall
have all new buses."

"Wonderful!" said Uncle Freddie.

"I will buy them at once,"
said Mr. Kingman.

And that is just what he did.

Jimmy Finds a Way

"Get ready, Jimmy," said Mrs. Young.
"You should have been ready long ago.
The school bus will be here soon."

"I don't want to take the bus today,"
said Jimmy. "I will not know any
of the boys and girls."

His mother laughed and said, "How could
you know any of them? This is only
your first day in a new school. You will soon
make friends, just as you did in Garden City."

"I know," said Jimmy. "But would you
please take me to school in the car?"

"All right," said Mrs. Young.

124

Jimmy and his family now lived in the country.
They had left Garden City just a week ago.

Every day Mr. Young took a train
into the city where he worked.
Now he was ready to go to the station.

"Come on, Jimmy," Mr. Young called.
"You may ride with Mother and me
to the station. Then Mother will
take you to school."

Jimmy jumped into the car. "First the station,"
he thought. "And then my new school!"

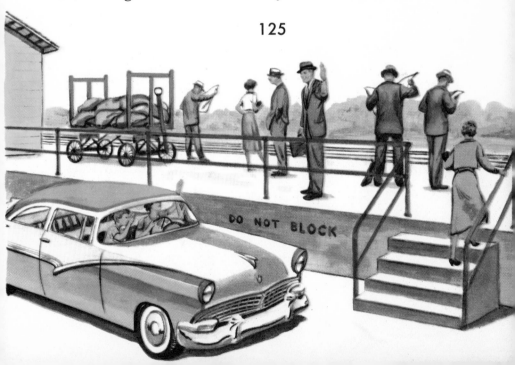

DO NOT BLOCK

That evening Jimmy told his father
and mother about his new school. "I guess
I will like it," he said. "But I miss
my old friends in Garden City."

"You will for a time, Jimmy," said his father.
"But you will soon make new friends."

"That's what mother told me,"
said Jimmy. "But what should I do?"

"You will find a way," said Mr. Young.
"And now, Jimmy, it's time for you
to go to sleep. We will see you in the morning."

The next morning Jimmy was up early.
He waited around in the kitchen
for something to eat.

"My, you're up early," said his mother.
"Did you have a good sleep, Jimmy?"

"Yes, but I couldn't get to sleep
right away," Jimmy answered.

"Why not?" asked his mother.

"I thought about friends last night,"
said Jimmy. "I wanted to find a way
to make new ones."

"And did you?" asked his mother.

"Maybe," said Jimmy with a smile.
"Maybe I did."

When Mr. Young came into the kitchen,
he said, "I have to hurry.
I want to catch an early train
to the city."

"I have to hurry, too," said Jimmy.

"I'm on my way now. See you after school!"

"How will you get to school
this morning?" asked Mr. Young.

"On the school bus," answered Jimmy.

Then he ran out of the house
as fast as his legs would go.

He took his new ball along with him.

Mr. and Mrs. Young looked at
each other and smiled.

"Jimmy will get along all right,"
said Mr. Young. "He knows how to make friends."

Jimmy ran all the way to the bus stop, where other children were waiting.

"Hello," said Jimmy.

"Hello," said one of the boys. "We saw you coming up the road as fast as your legs would go. What's your hurry?"

"I didn't want to miss the bus," said Jimmy.

"Anyone who can run so fast would make a good ballplayer," said another boy. "Why don't you get in our game today?"

"Thanks," said Jimmy. "I would like to play. And we can use my new ball."

Jimmy climbed on the bus with the boys and girls. "I know how to make friends," he thought. "I like my new school."

What Do You Think?   Interpreting character

Why didn't Jimmy want to take the school bus?
Why didn't Jimmy like school the first day?
Why couldn't he get to sleep that night?
What did Jimmy do first to make friends?
How will he keep his new friends?

A Clever Goat

Once, long ago, there was a goatkeeper.
Early in the morning he took his goats
up the hill to feed. Late in the evening
he took them home again.

There was one young goat
who would not walk with the others.
"Come along with us,"
the other goats said. "You must not feed
alone around here. A lion may get you."

The young goat laughed.
"I have never seen a lion
on this hill," she said. "I don't think
there is one."

Then one evening the little goat
saw some young green plants.
"They look very good," she said.
"I think I will stay here and eat them."

"No, no," said the other goats.
"Come on. You will not be safe alone."

"But I want to eat the plants,"
said the little goat. "I am hungry."

The other goats walked on, and
the little goat stayed and ate the plants.
Then she began to walk home alone.

All at once she saw a lion.

"Gr-r-r!" said the lion.

"Oh, my!" thought the goat.
"There IS a lion after all!
How hungry he looks! I must think
of something to do."

"GR-R-R-R!" said the lion again.

Then the goat said, "Good evening,
Mr. Lion. I am pleased to see you."

The lion was surprised. "Why are
you pleased?" he asked.
"You must know that I eat goats."

The goat said, "Yes, I knew it
long ago. But that is all right.
I know you must be hungry, so you
may eat me for your supper."

"How can you say that?" asked the lion.

"You have let us feed on your hill
for a long time," said the goat.
"Now I think it is time that we did
something for you."

The lion looked VERY surprised.

132

"Would you do one thing
before you eat me?" asked the goat.

"What is it?" asked the lion.

"Let me sing once before supper,"
the goat said. "I am a wonderful singer."

"You may sing," said the lion.
"I am hungry, but I can wait."

"Thank you," said the goat.
"Now will you please sit on that rock?
One should never stand
next to a singer."

The lion climbed onto the rock.

Then the goat called, "B-a-a! B-a-a!"

"Is that all?" asked the lion,
who knew very little about singing.

"Oh, no!" said the goat. "Just wait!"

133

Again she called, "B-a-a! B-a-a!"
This "B-a-a! B-a-a!" could be heard
far away.

The goatkeeper heard her call.
He ran up the hill as fast
as his legs would carry him.

When the lion saw the man,
he jumped off the rock and ran away.

The goatkeeper took the goat home.

When the other goats saw her,
they said, "See! We told you so!
We knew there was a lion on the hill."

"Yes, there was," said the young goat.
"But lions are not as clever
as goats."

Did You Learn It in the Story?
Goats feed high up on a hill.
Goats eat young green plants.
Young lions have black spots.
Lions run away when they see people.

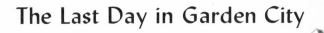

The Last Day in Garden City

It was time for Pat and Joe
to leave Garden City.
And they wanted to buy
some things to take home.

Mrs. Turner took them to one
of the big stores in town.
Mary and Dick went along, too.

"Is this all one store?" Pat asked.

"Yes," said Mary. "There are things
to buy on every floor."

On the first floor Pat and Joe found
a box of candy for their mother.

"Let me carry it," said Joe.

Then they found some letter paper
for Aunt Mary and Uncle Jack.

Pat and Joe could not find anything
for their father. They looked and looked.

At last Mrs. Turner said, "Children,
let's stop looking around now. We're all hungry.
I think we should go somewhere to eat."

"Where shall we go?" Pat asked.

"There is a place to eat on the roof
of this store," said Mrs. Turner.

They took the elevator to the roof,
where a waiter showed them to a table.
Mrs. Turner thanked him. "This is
a good place," she said.

"Look how high up we are!" said Mary.

"I see a garden on the roof," said Joe.
"May we go out and look at it?"

"Let's go now before we eat," said Mrs. Turner.
"Leave your boxes on the table."

They went out to see the roof garden
and stood looking over the city.
Far, far down they could see the river.

Pat said, "That boat down there
looks like the boat we came on."

"And see the bridge," said Dick.
"That is Singing River Bridge."

"Everything looks so little!" said Joe.

They stood and looked at the bridge
for a long time.

Then Joe said, "I'm hungry. Let's eat."

"All right," said Mrs. Turner.

They went back to their table.

As they sat down Pat said, "Joe,
what did you do with Mother's candy?"

"I thought I put it on the table," said Joe.
He looked around, but he didn't see the box.

"You must have put it
on some other table," said Mrs. Turner.
"Look again. Maybe you will find it."

Joe stood up and looked all around.
At another table he saw a girl opening a box.

"Oh!" said Joe. "That girl has my box!"

Before anyone could stop him, Joe ran over
to the little girl. "Hello," he said.
"Did you find my box of candy?"

"No," said the girl. "I don't have
any candy. I have a new book."

She showed it to Joe. It was
a wonderful book filled with pictures.

"See!" said the girl. "Look at all
the pictures of Garden City."

"Father would like that," said Joe.

Just then Pat came over to see
what was going on. He liked the book.
"Let's give Father a book like this one," he said.

"We could look at it, too," said Joe.

"Where is Mother's candy?"
Pat asked.

"I haven't found it," Joe answered.

As they were talking, a waiter came
up to them. He had a box in his hand.
"Is this your box?" he asked.

"Oh, yes, that's Mother's candy,"
said Joe.

"You left it at the foot of a tree
in the roof garden," said the waiter.
"Did you think it would grow?"

"I wish it would," said Joe, laughing.
"Then we could have lots of candy."

"Thank you," Pat said to the waiter.
"It's a good thing you found our box."

Then he and Joe went back to the table
where the Turners were waiting.

"Now we can eat!" said Joe.

When they were through eating, they went
down to another floor. There Pat and Joe
found a book for their father.

"Whenever we look at the pictures,
we will think of Garden City," Pat said.

"We will miss you," said Mary.
"I wish you didn't have to go home."

"We will miss you, too," said Pat.
"Maybe you can come to see us."

"Oh, yes," said Joe. "You would like
Springfield. We don't have any roof gardens.
But we can take you for a boat ride."

"We will come!" said Mary and Dick.

TO TRAINS

The City

Jack took an elevator.
　　Jack climbed high
Up a big building
　　Into the sky.

Far, far under him
　　As Jack looked down,
He could see the city
　　Like a little toy town.

Little people walking
　　In and out of doors,
Buying coats and hats and shoes
　　In little toy stores.

Red trucks and blue trucks
　　Made a singing noise.
Black cars, brown cars,
　　Just like toys!

142

Study Pages

Sound of the Vowel u in up

You know the sound of **u** in **up, fun,**
and **must**. Say the sound.

Now say the words **uncle, supper,**
and **hungry**. How many parts does each
word have? Say the first part of each
word. Say the vowel sound heard
in the first part of each word.

Does a glass dog ever get hungry?

Do people have supper in the morning?

Sound of the Vowel e in egg

You know the sound of **e** in **egg, went,**
and **red**. Say the sound.

Say the words **Betty, clever,** and
yellow. Say the first part of each
word again. Say the vowel sound heard
in the first part of each word.

Is a clown in a yellow hat ever clever?

Words with Two Parts

Say the word **sleeping**. How many parts does it have? What is the first part? What is the vowel sound in the first part?

Say the first part of **keeping**, **reading**, **landing**, and **waiting**. Then say the vowel sound in each first part.

Here are other words with two parts that you know. Say the first part of each word and its vowel sound.

needed	supper	Mary	happen
planted	clever	carry	kitchen
painted	sister	hurry	open

Where are cookies made?
What did you eat last night?
Who is Dick's sister?

What Are They Called?

Use the words **Animals**, **Clothes**, **Family**, **Letters**, **Names**, **Buildings**, and **Plants**.

lion	woodchuck	goat
hat	shoes	coat
hen	kitten	horse
flower	corn	tree
Betty	George	Mr. Long

monkey	pig	rabbit	cat
aunt	uncle	sister	father
A	B	C	D
barn	house	station	school

Think of what the following are called.

one	two	three	four
milk	egg	pie	apple
sister	mother	aunt	girl

Short Vowel Sounds

You know that the vowel is short in
an, **men**, **sing**, and **must**.

Here are some other words you know.
Say each one and its vowel sound.
Then say again all the words with short
vowel sounds.

land	left	think	bus
ate	need	ice	use

Here are some new words with short
vowel sounds. Say each one.

cap	pet	bill	sun
glad	fell	still	

Find the one that would be
in a box of clothes.

What word is pictured?

Garden City Days

Seesaw the Duck

One day the Turners went for a drive along Singing River. They liked to get away from the city whenever they could.

"Let's stop at this farm," said Mrs. Turner. "I need some eggs."

"Let's do," said Dick. "I want to see the farm animals."

"I do, too," said Mary. "I wish we had a pet at home."

Her father laughed as he turned the car into the farmyard. "No pets in the city!" he said. "A farm is the place for animals."

144

After looking around the farm,
the Turners were on their way at last.

"Did you see the little ducks?"
Mrs. Turner asked. "There were five
of them in the barnyard."

"Quack!" said a voice in the car.

"What did you say?" asked Mrs. Turner
as she looked around at the children.
"Oh, the top of the egg basket is
jumping up and down! What's in it?"

A funny look came over Mary's face.
She opened the basket, and there was
a little yellow duck.

"The farmer's wife gave him to us,"
Mary said. "Please let us keep him
for a pet."

"Please, may we?" asked Dick.

"We cannot keep a duck in the city,"
said Mr. Turner. "We must take him back."

But Mrs. Turner said, "No, it's
after five. We have to get home.
This evening we must hold a family talk."

After supper the family sat
around the table.

Mary brought the duck to the table
and put him on a piece of newspaper.

"Quack, quack," he said.

"My, this little duck talks a lot,"
said Mr. Turner.

"Yes, but he is so small he will not
make a lot of noise," said Dick.

"That's right," said Mary. "He's just
a baby duck. I know he will keep still."

"He will not stay small forever,"
said Mr. Turner.

"If he gets too big, we can have
another family talk," said Mary.

"All right, then," said Mr. Turner.
"If he keeps still, he may stay with us."

The children's faces looked very happy.
And the duck opened his yellow bill.
"Quack! Quack!" he said.

"He's saying thank you," said Mary.
"And he says he wants a name."

The little duck walked over to Mary.
First he put one leg out to the right and down.
Then he put the other leg out to the left
and down.

"He looks like a seesaw when he walks,"
laughed Dick. "Let's call him Seesaw."

147

In the days that followed,
Seesaw had lots of fun.
He went everywhere the children
went. He made friends with many
of the neighbors. He did not make
any noise. He was a good pet.

When he was five weeks old, Seesaw
went outdoors with Mary and Dick.
He jumped into some water he saw
in the yard and sailed about in it.
He was very happy.

When it was time to go in,
Seesaw did not want to leave the water.

He opened his bill. "QUACK!" he said.

"Oh! His voice has changed!" said Mary.

The children took Seesaw into the house.

"QUACK! QUACK!" said Seesaw.

"No, no!" said Dick. "Be still."

But Seesaw would not be still.

He quacked and quacked, day and night.

The neighbors did not like the noise.

So the Turners had another family talk.

The children's faces looked sad.

"Our pet is growing up," said Mrs. Turner.
"He isn't happy with us now."

"He will have to go," said Mr. Turner.
"Shall we take him back to the farm?"

"QUACK!" said Seesaw.

"He doesn't want to go back to the farm,"
said Mary. "He says he would like
to live in the city park."

"That's a good thought," said Mr. Turner.

So the family took Seesaw to the park.

As soon as the duck saw the water
in the park, he ran to it. At once he
was sailing about with many other ducks.

"Look at him go!" said Dick. "He will
have fun with the other ducks."

"He likes it here," said Mary.

Every week the Turners went to see
their pet.

One day he followed them to the car.

Mary said, "Look, Mother! Seesaw wants
to come with us. Please let him come,
just for one night."

So the duck stayed all night
in his old home.

The next day the Turners took him back
to the park. He did not quack once.

"He doesn't need to quack,"
said Dick. "He is happy now."

Waiting for Santa Claus

Where was Santa Claus?

He had said in his letter, "Look
for me on the day before Christmas.
I will come to your schoolroom
at three."

Now the clock said four,
and Santa Claus had not come.

The children watched and
waited in the schoolroom.
The Christmas tree waited, too.

On the tree were red apples and
little baskets of Christmas candy.

Everything was ready for the party.
But where was Santa Claus?

Bill Newman opened the door and looked out over the park. Snow was everywhere. But no Santa Claus!

"Santa Claus always comes to our Christmas party," said Dick Turner.

"Maybe he cannot get through the snow," said Mary. "There's lots of snow this winter."

"It snows every winter, but Santa Claus always comes," said Bill.

"Maybe we should have our party right now," said Miss Fielding.

"Oh, no!" said the children.

Just then they heard a noise.

"It's Santa Claus!" they said.

"Here he is at the door!"

"Come in!" the children called.
"We're ready for the party.
We have apples, candy, and cake."
"Come out!" Santa Claus called.
"Put on your warm clothes.
We have work to do
before we can have our party."

The children could not guess
what Santa Claus was talking about.
But they put on their hats, coats,
and overshoes and ran out.
On Santa Claus's sled were
many small boxes and one big box.
"Santa Claus, are all the presents
for us?" the children asked.
"Some of them are," he said. "And I
have brought some other presents, too.
Come with me."

The children followed Santa Claus
into the park.

"Look at the little birds
in the snow," said Santa Claus.

"The birds!" said Bill. "We didn't
think of them! They must be hungry."

"They are," said Santa Claus.
"I have brought some corn for them."

"Corn isn't enough," said Dick.
"Let's give the birds some presents,
too. We can give them apples
and pieces of our Christmas cake."

The children ran into the school.
They brought back a big piece
of their cake and many apples.

154

Santa Claus was waiting for them
in the park. He was standing
near a little pine tree.

"Oh, Santa Claus," said Dick.
"Now I know why you were late.
You were looking for a Christmas tree
for the birds. And here are
the presents."

The children put pieces
of Christmas cake near the treetop.
Then they put apples and corn
on the tree.

"Now the tree is ready,"
said Santa Claus. "If we stand
very still, the birds will come and eat."

The children stood nearby and waited.

Down came the hungry birds.
They ate and ate.

At last Santa Claus said,
"The birds have had their party.
Now we can have ours."

They went back to the school
and ate their cake and apples.
They had milk to drink, too.

After that, Santa Claus gave
each boy and girl a small present.

Then Santa Claus opened the big box
that he had brought on his sled.
It was filled with pieces of wood.

"What are they for?" asked Dick.

"To make a feeding station
for the birds," said Santa Claus.

"Good!" said the children. "Now the birds
can have Christmas all winter long."

The Kitten That Traveled

Mary and Dick Turner were
in the play yard. All at once
they heard a dog barking.

"It must be the new little dog
next door," said Mary. "Why do
you think he is barking?"

Just then a small white kitten
ran into the yard. The kitten was
followed by a little brown dog.

Dick ran after the dog. "Stop that!"
he called. "Go home! Go home!"

The little brown dog ran away
as fast as his legs could carry him.
The kitten stayed in the yard.

"Meow!" said the kitten.

"Poor thing!" said Mary. "She's hungry.
I will get her some milk to drink."

When Mary came back, Dick said,
"I don't think this kitten has a home.
I wish we could keep her."

"Maybe we can," said Mary.
"Let's ask Mother. Now that our duck
lives in the park, we need a new pet."

"Let's think of a good name
for this kitten," said Dick.

Mary said, "Look at her little paws.
They are as white as snow. I would
like to call her Snow Paws."

Mrs. Turner said they could keep
the new pet if no one came for her.

No one did. So the children gave
Snow Paws a present to wear. It said

> Snow Paws
>
> 554 Bridge Street
>
> Garden City

Snow Paws was happy with the Turners,
but she did not like the little brown dog.
Whenever he came close to her,
Snow Paws always backed away.

One day the dog came so close that
Snow Paws turned and ran. She ran
until she was far away from home.

Snow Paws ran until she came
to a farm close by the road.
She saw a truck standing in the barnyard.

Snow Paws climbed into the back
of the truck and jumped into a basket.
Soon she was sleeping.

When the farmer came to drive
the truck away, Snow Paws never woke up.
She was still sleeping when the truck
came to a stop far down the road.

All at once her nose told her there were
animals close by. Then Snow Paws woke up!

She looked out through an opening
in the basket and saw trees and walks.

Snow Paws was in the city park!

Every day the farmer brought feed
and hay for the park animals.
This time he had parked his truck
near the lion house.

Snow Paws heard something say, "Gr-r-r-r!"
She looked out and saw five lions close by!
What a noise they made!

"Oh, what will happen to me?"
thought Snow Paws.

But the lions could not hurt her.
They were fenced in.

Just then the basket fell
off the truck, and out fell Snow Paws.

"Where did you come from?" said the farmer.

Then he saw her name and the name
of her street.

"So you live in Garden City!"
he said. "I will take you home."

Again Snow Paws rode in the truck.

This time she went home.

Mary and Dick saw the truck drive up.

"Is this your kitten?" asked the farmer.

"She fell out of one of my baskets.

Then she rode with me all over the city.

She has traveled a long way today!"

"Oh, thank you," said Mary.

"Snow Paws!" she said to the kitten.

"Why did you run away?"

Snow Paws did not answer. Just then
the little brown dog came along. He barked
and barked, but Snow Paws did not run away.

She looked at him as if to say,

"Oh! You are only a little dog.

I have met lions!"

What Do You Think?   Main idea and details

What Happens?
A kitten learns that a dog cannot hurt her.
A dog finds a kitten in a city park.
A lion gets a new home.

The Shoes That Were Danced to Pieces

Long ago there was a king who had
seven children. All of them were girls.

The seven sisters had many pretty clothes.
But they always needed new shoes.

When the sisters went to bed,
their shoes were as good as new.
Each morning their shoes were
danced to pieces! But no one ever
saw the girls leave their beds.

At last the king said,
"You girls wear out too many shoes.
What do you do with all the shoes
I buy for you?"

The seven sisters only laughed
and would not tell.

"I do not like secrets,"
said the king. "I will find out
what the girls are doing."

So he asked one of his men
to watch the girls' bedroom door.
But the watchman went to sleep.

The king said, "I must find out
where the girls go to dance.
If anyone can tell me, he shall
have one of the girls for a wife.
Some day he shall be king."

Many young men came.
One by one they were told
to watch the girls' bedroom.

But they always went to sleep.
Not one woke up in time
to learn the sisters' secret.

One day a young woodsman rode
down from the hills. As he rode along,
he met an old woman.

"Where are you going?" she asked.

He answered, "I am going to see
the seven sisters. I hope to learn
where they go to dance."

The old woman said, "If you would
learn the secret, do just as I say.
Do not drink anything that the sisters
may give you."

Then she handed him a cap, saying,
"Take this magic cap. When you
wear it, no one can see you."

The young man thanked her
and rode on.

165

Soon the woodsman came before the king.
"Oh, King," he said. "I hope to learn
the secret of the seven sisters."

"I hope you will," said the king.
"I am about to give up."

Then he gave the woodsman
some good clothes and asked him to supper.

After supper the oldest sister
handed the young man a drink.
When no one was looking, he put
the drink in some of the plants nearby.

When the sisters went to their room,
he put on his magic cap. Then he
waited close by their door.

Soon the sisters came out of the room,
dressed for a party.

166

Then the oldest sister opened
a secret door in the floor.

"Sisters, let us go," she said.
"Do not step on your dresses."

They walked down secret steps.
The woodsman followed, wearing
his magic cap. No one could see him.

Soon they all came to a wonderful woods,
where the trees had leaves of gold.
The woodsman took some leaves with him.

Next they came to a river, where seven boats
were waiting. In each boat sat a young man.

Each man took one of the sisters
over the river. The woodsman rode
in the oldest sister's boat.

Soon they were on land once again.
Before them stood a lighted building, with doors
opening into a ballroom. The sisters
went in and began to dance.
How light their steps were!

They danced until five
in the morning. By that time
their shoes were danced to pieces.
So everyone went home.

Once again the woodsman followed
the sisters over the river.
He followed them through the woods
and up the secret steps.

The seven sisters put away
their party dresses. They took off
their shoes and went to bed.

The next day the king asked
the woodsman what he had found out.

"I have learned the secret," he said.
And he told what he had seen.

"It is all a story," the girls laughed.
"He has been sleeping all night."

"Oh, no, I haven't," said the woodsman
as he showed the wonderful leaves.

"No one but you could learn
the secret," the king said.
"Now you may ask for a wife."

"I like the oldest sister best,"
said the young man. "She is the fairest."

The oldest sister smiled and
gave him her hand. And they
were happy ever after.

169

A Boat Show

Dick Turner and Bill Newman stood on Singing River Bridge. They were watching the boats in the river.

All at once a big red flying boat landed on the water.

"I like that boat," said Dick. "I'll build a flying boat for the boat show at school."

"I think I'll build an old-time sailboat," said Bill. "I hope my boat will get the prize."

"We will see," laughed Dick. "I think my boat will get the prize."

The two boys went to Dick's house
and began to work on their boats.
They were busy until supper time,
but they did not help each other.

"Do you want to hold this wood
so that I can saw it?" Dick asked.

"Not now," said Bill. "I'm busy."

After a time he asked Dick, "Will you
help me put the sails on my boat?"

"I'm busy now," said Dick. "I have
to finish my flying boat."

Just then they heard a noise in the next room.
They went to see what it was.

Polly Newman and Mary Turner were
busy working at a big table.

"Polly and I are building two boats
for the show," Mary told the boys.

Dick laughed. "I didn't know girls
could build boats," he said.

"Polly and I are a team," said Mary. "We help
each other. We're building a team of boats, too."

"They look like work boats," said Bill.

"They are," said Polly. "See, one is
long, and the other is short.
Do you think we will get the prize?"

"No," laughed Dick. "You see boats
like that every day on the river."

172

The boys and girls were busy all week.
At last the boats were finished,
and the children took them to school.
They placed them on tables brought
into the room for the show.
There were short boats and long boats,
sailing boats and fishing boats.

Miss Fielding liked the show.
"Now we are finished!" she said.
"Let's call Mr. Bridgeman into the room.
He will give a prize for the best boat."

After a short time, Mr. Bridgeman came.
He was pleased with all the boats.
"What good work!" he said.
"You must have been very busy!
This is a wonderful boat show."

Then he walked to the first table.

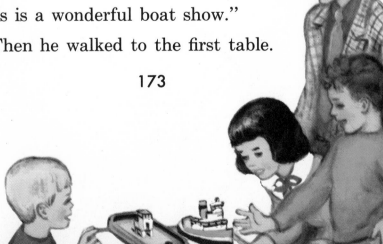

"Here is a good flying boat,"
said Mr. Bridgeman. "See how strong it is.
And here is an old-time sailboat. Whoever
made this one knew about sailboats."

He looked at each boat in the show.
"All the boats are good," he said.
"I cannot name the one best boat.
But I can tell you the TWO best."

"Oh!" thought Dick and Bill.

"They are a team of work boats,"
said Mr. Bridgeman. "They are
strong little boats. I think they're
the strongest in the show."

Miss Fielding smiled. "The work boats
were made by a team of girls," she said.

"They get the prize," said Mr. Bridgeman.

What Do You Think?   Definite and indefinite terms

Can you tell how long the boys and girls
work on their boats?

Can you tell how many boats are in the show?

Can you tell how many boats get the prize?

174

A Rolling Garden

On a little hill in the country
stood a little house. In the house
lived a little girl with yellow pigtails.
Her name was Penny, and she lived
with her Uncle George.

Uncle George was a gardener.
In his garden grew many good things to eat.

Penny had a garden, too. It was
a pretty little flower garden.
Penny planted the seeds and watered them.
From the seeds grew plants with flowers
of every color.

Uncle George told everyone,
"Oh, you should see Penny's garden!"

Every week Uncle George would fill
his wagon with garden things.
Then he would drive his team of horses
to the city.

Storekeepers were happy to buy
his country things.

Penny wanted to go to the city, too.
She wanted to see the wonderful buildings
and the crowds of people.

Uncle George always said, "I'll be busy
all day in the city. Anyway, you wouldn't like
the city. It's very hot and crowded there."

So Penny stayed at home and worked
in her flower garden. Her flowers
grew and grew.

Penny had a pet goat
that pulled a little wagon.

One day she said, "I'll play
that I'm going to the city."

So she filled her wagon with flowers.
She climbed up on the wagon
and rode to see all the neighbors.

"Take some flowers," she said.
"I grew them from seeds.
Take as many as you like."

The neighbors were glad to see Penny,
and they were glad to have flowers.
So every day Penny would put flowers
into her wagon. Then she would get in,
and off she would go.

One day Uncle George said, "Penny,
I have a surprise for you. Today
you may drive to town with me!"

Penny felt very happy. "Good!" she said.
"I'm glad I'll get to go today."

So she climbed into the wagon
with Uncle George. And the team
headed down the road.

Before long, the wagon rolled
into the city. How hot it was there!
The houses were close to one another.
The buildings looked as high as the sky.

Penny looked at the busy crowds
of people hurrying along the hot streets.
She didn't like what she saw.

"Uncle George, where are the trees
and flowers?" she asked.

178

"There is no room for them in the city,"
said Uncle George. "All the land here
is needed for buildings."

"Where do the children play
in this crowded city?" Penny asked.

"They play in the parks," he answered.

Just then a wagon filled with flowers
rolled down the street. People came
to buy the flowers.

How glad Penny felt! "This is the best thing
I have seen in the city," she said.
"It's a rolling flower garden."

When they went home, Penny thought
of nothing but the rolling garden.
She thought of it for days.

179

At last she talked to Uncle George.
She said, "I could fill my wagon
with flowers and drive to the city.
People would be glad to buy my flowers."

"Do you think your goat will be good?"
Uncle George asked. "He may run away."

"Oh, he never runs away,"
said Penny.

"All right, then," said Uncle George.

So the next week, when Uncle George
went to town, Penny went, too.
Her wagon looked like a rolling garden.

The goat was good on the country roads.
But when he saw the crowded city streets,
he began to run.

"Stop! Stop!" called Uncle George,
hurrying along after him.

But the goat would not stop.

The goat ran until he saw a park.
Then at last he came to a stop.

Crowds of children stood there,
holding flowers of many colors.

A small boy with a dog called to Penny,
"Will you be in our Spring Parade?"

"I didn't know there was to be
a Spring Parade," answered Penny.

"Your goat knew," laughed the boy.

Just then Uncle George came along
with his team and wagon.
"Are you all right, Penny?" he asked.

"Yes," said Penny. "I came
just in time for the parade!"

181

Old Bill and the Flowers

Old Bill was made of wood and hay.
His arms and legs were wood.
His funny-looking clothes were filled
with hay.

Bill stood alone in the cornfield
back of the farmhouse. He stood there
in winter, spring, summer, and fall.
He watched to see that the big birds
did not eat the corn.

He was a good watchman.

But one hot summer day,
Old Bill felt sad.

"Corn! Corn!" he said. "That's all
I see all summer. I wish I could be
in another place. Then I could see
new faces and make new friends."

The strong summer wind heard the wish.

"Poor Bill!" thought the wind. "He stands there in the hot sun. I'll get busy and help him."

So the wind went to the hens.

"Old Bill wants to see new faces," said the wind. "Will you let him stand near your house?'

"No, we can't have him here," said the hens. "He looks too funny."

So the wind went to the animals in the barnyard.

"Old Bill stands in the hot sun all summer long," said the wind. "Will you let him come here?"

"Oh, no," said the animals. "We can't have him here."

So the strong summer wind went on.
It went to the flower garden.

"Will you have old Bill here
for a change?" asked the wind.

The sunflower said, "We would like
to help old Bill. But he does look
very funny!"

Then a small blue flower said,
"Let Bill stand near us. We could
dress him up. We could grow
all over him. We could take
care of him."

"But how could he get here?"
asked the sunflower.

The wind said, "I'll take care
of that. Leave it to me."

That night the wind began to blow.
It pulled Old Bill out of the cornfield.
On and on it went with him,
until it came to the garden.

When Old Bill woke up next morning,
his legs were planted in a new place.

"Where am I?" he asked.

"You are with us," said the flowers.
"We are going to take care of you."

They began to climb all over him.
Blue and yellow flowers grew
over his coat and cap.

When the small birds saw him,
they said, "It can't be Old Bill."

"It is," laughed the flowers,
"He came to live with us."

185

Old Bill was happy in the garden.

He did not keep the small birds away.

They could not hurt anything there.

But after a time he thought

of the cornfield.

"Maybe the big birds are eating

the corn," he said. "I should

go back and take care of things.

But I shall miss my friends here."

"Some of us will go with you,"

said the flowers.

So Old Bill went back to the field,

wearing his new flower clothes.

"Hello, Bill," laughed the corn.

"How wonderful you look! It is

good to have you home!"

What Do You Think?   Indexing

Find the four times of the year.
Find two places where Old Bill stood.
Find two colors of flowers.

Study Pages

First Consonant Sounds: Two Letters

smile	snow	small	short
prize	pretty	place	present
drink	bridge	dress	drive
green	truck	grew	friend
glass	floor	blow	glad
clock	climb	close	sleep
cream	brought	crowd	change

First Consonant Sounds: Three Letters

three	Christmas	thought	through
street	travel	strong	story

Last Consonant Sounds: Two Letters

pla**nt**	aunt	present	felt
thi**nk**	land	thank	drink
si**ng**	strong	bridge	young

A color, first sound of **gr**?

A woman, last sound of **nt**?

Parts er and est

Betty, who is seven years old, is a young girl. Five-year-old John is younger. Four-year-old George is the youngest of all the children.

Who is the oldest of all three?

The **er** of **younger** tells about two children. The **est** of **youngest** tells about three or many people.

John was standing one foot from the river. Bill was three feet away. Joe was four feet away.

Who was nearest to the water?

What can go faster?
   a clown, a train
   a woodchuck, a horse

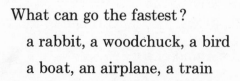

What can go the fastest?
   a rabbit, a woodchuck, a bird
   a boat, an airplane, a train

How Old? How Many?

Very soon baby rabbits leave
their home.

How old are baby rabbits when they
leave their home? Does **very soon** tell
you how many days old they are?

When baby rabbits are three weeks
old, they can find what they need to eat.

How old are baby rabbits when they
can find something good to eat? What
words tell you?

What do the underlined words tell you?

There are many rabbits in the woods
and gardens of our country.

Baby rabbits see nothing for about
one week.

Jack rabbits can jump a long way.

After feeding all night, rabbits go
to bed early in the morning.

Sounds You Know	New Words

o in **not**   shop

i in **sit**

and

x in **box**   fix

ch in **change**

and

air in **fair**   chair

e in **step**

and **nd** in **found**   send

r in **rock**

and **each**   reach

Long **i** and

e with no sound   write

Last Parts of Words

er of **older**   shorter, stronger

est of **oldest**   shortest, strongest

Does a chair have paws and legs?

Does everyone write with the right hand?

Do rocking chairs have rocks?

Singing River Secrets

The Clock Shop

Mr. Hope felt sad whenever he walked
by the big stores on Kingman Street.

Every morning he walked by them
on the way to his little clock shop.
Every morning he saw the new things
in the big stores.

"People like to buy things that
are new," thought Mr. Hope. "I wish
I had a few new clocks in my shop."

Mr. Hope had the smallest shop
on the street. He was too poor to buy
new clocks. He had only old clocks
in his little shop.

There were clocks that people
had brought to be fixed. There were
clocks that no one wanted at all.
Mr. Hope fixed them, too.

"I like old clocks," he thought.
"If I fix them up, people may want
to buy them."

But very few people did.
So the shop was crowded
with old clocks. They stood
on the tables and chairs.
Only the chair where Mr. Hope sat
had no clocks on it.

189

One day Mr. Hope was fixing
an old clock. It was made like a bird,
with long gold legs and a short tail.

Every hour the bird's bill fell open,
and the bird told the time.

"This is the best clock I ever had,"
Mr. Hope thought. "I hope no one will ever
buy it. I would like to keep it always."

Just then he saw a boy and a girl
standing before the shop.

"What wonderful clocks!" said the girl.

"Why don't you come in and
look around?" Mr. Hope asked.

190

The children came into the shop.

"I'm Frank Summers," said the boy.

"This is my sister Polly."

The children looked at a few of the clocks.

"I like the flowered kitchen clock," said Polly.

"I like that red clock," said Frank.

Then they saw the bird clock.

They heard it tell the hour.

"Oh, this is the best clock
in the shop!" said Polly.

"I like it best, too," said Mr. Hope.

Frank said, "I wish we could stay
and look at it. But we must go now.
We must buy a present for Uncle John."

So the children left the clock shop.

Mr. Hope sat in his chair, thinking,
"If only I had some new clocks!
Maybe then Polly and Frank
could have found a present here."

He went back to work on the clocks
that needed fixing.

In about an hour, he heard voices
at the door. Frank and Polly were back.
Their faces looked sad.

"What happened?" asked Mr. Hope.

"We went to all the big stores,"
said Frank. "We didn't have
enough money to buy a present."
He showed Mr. Hope the money he had.

"Uncle John is our best uncle,"
said Polly. "How can we buy anything
good enough with so little money?"

Mr. Hope smiled at the children.
Then he said, "You have enough money
to buy my bird clock with the gold legs."

"That wonderful clock!" said Polly.

"That clock you like best!" said Frank.

"Yes," said Mr. Hope. "I know it
isn't new. But your uncle may like it."

"I know he will," said Frank.
"It's a wonderful present."

The clock told the hour
as the children left the shop.

Mr. Hope smiled as he watched them go.
"I don't care if I have nothing
but old clocks," he thought.
"I have made two children happy."

The Sun Tree

Once upon a time an old woman
lived in a small house near the woods.
She lived all alone with her pet bird.
He called "Good day" to anyone who
came to the house.

People liked the old woman.
They liked her little house, for
it was always filled with warm light.
The light did not come from the sun.
It came from a flowering apple tree
that stood close by the door.

Throughout the year the tree had
wonderful white flowers and apples.
The apples were as gold as the sun,
and they gave out a warm sunlight.

So the tree was called the Sun Tree.

Sometimes the neighbors wished
that they had Sun Trees, too.
Then the old woman would reach up
and get an apple from the tree.

"Plant a seed from this apple,"
she would say. "If you take good care
of it, you may have a Sun Tree, too."

When the neighbors reached home,
they planted their seeds.
However, not everyone knew how to care
for them. A few seeds grew, but many did not.

No tree ever grew to be so wonderful
as the old woman's Sun Tree.

The king heard about the Sun Tree
and rode over to see it.
He looked at its gold apples and
snow-white flowers.

"I must have this tree," he said.
"In the morning I shall send my men
to get it."

The old woman answered, "Oh, King,
I planted the tree and took care of it.
It reaches high over my house. It is my tree."

"But it is on my land," said the king.
"So it is MY tree."

"It can't live if you carry it
away," said the old woman.

196

"All right," said the king.
"I'll take an apple seed.
But if the seed does not grow,
I'll send my men for the tree."

The king's gardeners planted the seed
and cared for it in every way.
Still, it did not grow.

So early one morning, the king's men
came to the old woman. "The king wishes
to have this tree at once," they said.

The men took the tree away. They let
the old woman keep only one apple.

She planted a seed, and it grew
into another Sun Tree.

Now the Sun Tree that was planted
near the king's door did not live.

One day the king heard
that the old woman had a new Sun Tree.
So he rode over to see her.

"It must be that the Sun Tree needs
this land to grow in," he told her.
"I shall build a large house here.
You must find another home."

"I have always lived here,"
said the old woman. "Do not send me away.
I can't bear to leave my Sun Tree."

"It is MY land and MY Sun Tree,"
said the king. "So hurry!"

"May I take an apple with me?"
the old woman asked.

"Not one apple," answered the king.

The old woman took her pet bird
and walked out of the yard.
Neighbors helped carry her things
to another house down the road.

As they left, the bird called
to the king, "Just you wait!"

But the king only smiled. He was
thinking of the large house he would build.
He was thinking of the way the Sun Tree
would light his rooms.

At last the king's house was finished.
He asked all his friends to come to a party.

When the friends reached the house,
they went through its many large rooms.

The king said, "See how everything
catches the light from my Sun Tree!"

"But look!" said a friend.
"What is your tree doing?"

The Sun Tree was going up, up, up.
Out of the garden it sailed.
High, high into the sky it went
like a large gold and white bird.

It sailed on and on until it
reached the old woman's door.
There it stayed, and there it grew.

This time the king did not send
his men to get the tree.
He had learned that not everything
upon his land was his.

What Do You Think?   Analysis of sentences (subjects, objects)

Many people wished that they had Sun Trees.
Who wished something?   What did they wish?

The Young Newsboy

Almost everyone knew Big Bill.
He worked on the Garden City News,
the morning newspaper.

People would say, "Big Bill always writes
the best news story in the paper."

Almost no one knew Little Bill.
He wanted to write for the paper, too.

Every day he asked his father,
"When can I write for the paper?"

At last Big Bill said, "You can't write
for it now. But you are big enough to work
for it."

"What can I do?" Little Bill asked.

"You can be a newsboy," said his father.
"You can carry papers to people's houses.
That's the way I began."

"When can I do it?" Little Bill asked.

"In the morning," said Big Bill. "I'll take you
to the office and show you what to do."

Next morning Little Bill was up
very early. He didn't want to oversleep.

"Sh!" said Big Bill as they left
for the office. "Don't make any noise."

On the way they met the milkman.
Little Bill almost called, "Hello!"

"Sh! Be still!" his father said.
"A newsboy must not make any noise.
People may say he woke them up
too early."

A crowd of boys was waiting
at the newspaper office.

One boy said, "Hello, Big Bill.
Are you a newsboy again?"

"Right now I am," said Big Bill.

Soon a man came out of the office
and gave the boys the morning papers.

A few of the high-school boys had
cars to drive. Five boys had wagons.
Almost all the boys, like Bill,
just had bags on their backs.

Big Bill and Little Bill went
to River Street nearby. When they came
to the first house, a dog ran out.

"Always make friends with a watchdog,"
said Big Bill. "See, this is just
a young dog. He will not hurt you."

Little Bill gave the dog a pat.
Then he put the paper on the doorstep.

The dog did not bark.

"He likes me," said Little Bill.
"I've made friends with one dog anyway."

The next house had a fence around it.

"Never jump over fences," said Big Bill.
"If you can't get into the yard,
sail the paper onto the doorstep.
Use your strong right arm."

The next house was Miss Short's.

"I'll tell you a secret," said Big Bill.
"There's an apple tree in this yard.
I've heard that Miss Short doesn't care
if a newsboy takes some apples."

Little Bill went into the yard.
He found two yellow apples
and gave one to Big Bill.

"This is fun," said Little Bill.
"It will be fun in winter, too.
I'll carry papers on my sled."

Big Bill and Little Bill felt happy
as they walked from house to house.
At the foot of River Street
they saw Singing River.

"Singing River is a big help
to our newspaper," said Big Bill.

"How?" asked Little Bill.

"Away up the river are the woods,"
answered Big Bill. "All day long,
men are sawing down big pine trees.
Boats carry the wood to Springfield.
There it is made into paper."

"And is the paper used
for our newspaper?" asked Little Bill.

"Yes, it is," said Big Bill.

Little Bill said, "When I grow up,
I'll write a story about that.
I've learned a lot today."

"You will learn something
every day," said his father.

When they reached home,
Big Bill said, "Watch me!
I'll show you how I used my strong
right arm when I was on the ball team."

Little Bill watched. His father took
a paper. Up, up, up it sailed.
It did not land on the doorstep.
It fell on the roof.

Little Bill laughed. "You will never make
the team that way," he said.

Little Bill climbed to the roof
and brought the paper down.

"Maybe I can do it," he said.

This time the paper fell on the step.

"Good for you!" said Big Bill.
"Soon you will be the best newsboy
on the Garden City News."

Little Bill smiled. He hoped so, too.

The City Woodchuck

Once upon a time there was
a woodchuck who lived in the city.
He was the cleverest woodchuck
that ever lived.

He was so clever that he could
read and write!

But he was not happy. There were
no other woodchucks in the city.
So he was all alone.

One day he was reading the newspaper.
In it he found something that surprised
and pleased him. It said

Come to Mr. Magic
Mr. Magic Can Fix Everything
Let Him Help You
Room 243   Times Building

The woodchuck thought, "Maybe
Mr. Magic can help me. I'll go to see him."

He put on his cap and went out.
First he went to the Kingfish Eating Place,
where he ate some fish cakes.
Then he walked to the Times Building.

"Room 243," he told the elevator man.

"That room is two floors up,"
said the elevator man.

When the woodchuck reached
the right floor, he looked around.
He saw many large offices.

At last he found Mr. Magic's room.
On the glass door was painted

> Mr. Magic's Office
>
> Step Right In

In walked the woodchuck.

In an office chair sat Mr. Magic,
dressed all in black.

"How do you do?" he said
in woodchuck talk. "Please sit down."

"Oh!" said the woodchuck, holding out
his paw. "You know Woodchuck!"

"I know the talk of all the animals
and birds," said Mr. Magic.
"I've learned fish talk and bat talk, too.
Wish-sh-sh-sh is fish talk. Now what
can I do for you?"

The woodchuck looked sad.
"I hope you can help me," he said.
"I don't care for the crowded city.
I want to live in the country
like other woodchucks."

"Why did you come to this crowded city?"
asked Mr. Magic.

"I didn't come here," said the woodchuck.
"When I was young, I lived in a field.
But people came and put up buildings.
Little by little the city grew up
around me. Now here I am."

"Why did you come to see me?"
asked Mr. Magic.

"I want to go back to the country, but
I don't know how," said the woodchuck.

"Take an airplane," said Mr. Magic.

"Oh, no!" said the woodchuck.
"Please don't make me do that!"

"I know," said Mr. Magic. "I'll send
you to the country in a magic chair."

The woodchuck felt his chair turn
around and around. His head felt
very, very light. In a short time
he was sleeping.

When he woke up, he was
in the country, cold and hungry.
He wanted something to eat.

Many woodchucks were working
all around him.

"We must hurry to finish
our winter homes," they told him.
"You must get busy, too."

"First I'll get something
to eat," said the city woodchuck.

"Oh, there is nothing left
to eat," said a country woodchuck.

"Nothing to eat!"
said the city woodchuck. "Oh, my!
What shall I do?"

The country woodchuck said,
"Do as we do. We eat all summer
and sleep all winter. That's why we
build our homes before snow comes."

"But I don't want to sleep
all winter," said the city woodchuck.

He began to think of the safe,
warm city and the crowds of people.
He thought of the Kingfish Eating Place.
He thought of the good hot fish cakes
he used to eat there.

"I wish I were back in the city,"
he said.

Then he went to sleep.

The next thing the woodchuck knew,
he was back in Mr. Magic's office.

"My, but I'm glad to be here!"
he said. "The country is no place
for me. I'm a city woodchuck.
But I don't know what to do now."

"You should work," said Mr. Magic.
"Would you like to help me?"

"Oh, yes!" said the woodchuck. "How?"

"I need a helper in my office,"
said Mr. Magic. "Lots of animals come
to me. If you can learn their talk,
you can help me with my magic.
Now let us see if you can learn
fish talk. Say wish-sh-sh-sh."

"Watch-tch-tch-tch!" said the woodchuck.

"Not just right," smiled Mr. Magic.
"However, I know you will soon learn."

214

Where Was John ?

"Supper is ready," said Mrs. Early.
"Come and sit down."

Mr. Early came to the table in a hurry,
but John did not come at all.

"That's funny," said Mr. Early. "John is
always the first one here. Where can he be?"

"He's always so hungry," said Mrs. Early.
"And we have all the things he likes best
for supper. Where is that boy?
He must be busy somewhere."

John was a very busy boy. There were not enough hours in the day for all he had to do.

When he wasn't in school, he went to see his friends.

Sometimes he went to see Miss Green, who had an ice cream and candy shop.

Sometimes he went to the firehouse to see the firemen.

Sometimes he went to the police station to talk with Mr. Streeter, the policeman.

Sometimes he went to see Mr. Singer, the Fix-It Man, in his shop. There he helped him fix things.

Sometimes he played with Frank next door.

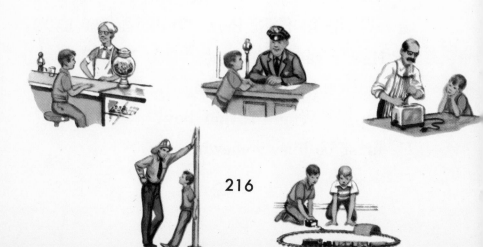

216

After doing all he had to do, John
was always very hungry. And he ALWAYS
came home for supper.

So now his father and mother were
surprised that John was late.

"Maybe he's at Miss Green's ice cream
and candy shop," said Mr. Early.

So he called Miss Green.
John was not there.

"He watches Mr. Singer fix things
sometimes," said Mrs. Early.

But John was not at the Fix-It Shop.

He wasn't at the firehouse.
He wasn't at the police station.

Then Mrs. Early said, "He must be
at Frank's house. Why didn't I
think of that before?"

But John was not there.

"Supper will be cold," said Mrs. Early.

"John should have come home on time,"
said Mr. Early. "Let's eat our supper.
Let's not wait for him."

They sat down at the table,
but they couldn't eat. They felt sad.

Soon they heard someone at the door.

"It's John!" said Mrs. Early, looking happy.

But it wasn't John. It was Miss Green.
After her, came a fireman. Then came Frank
and his mother with Mr. Streeter, the policeman.
Last came Mr. Singer, the Fix-It Man.

"Now, then, everyone," said Mr. Streeter,
the policeman. "We're going to find John.
Let's think. If you were John,
where would you be?"

"At my ice cream and candy shop,"
said Miss Green. "But John isn't there."

Mr. Singer, the Fix-It Man, said,
"Let me fix it. I think we must look
in the places where John wouldn't be."

So they looked under the chairs. They looked
up the chimney. They looked back of all the doors.

But John could not be found.

John's friends were ready to give up
when they heard a noise.

"That noise came from John's bedroom,"
said Mr. Early.

Everyone ran to see what was going on.

John met them at the door. "Hello,"
he said. "I had a good long sleep."

"Sleep!" said his father. "Is that
what you were doing?"

"Yes," said John. "I was sleepy."

Mr. Early laughed. "We never thought
of looking for you in bed," he said.

John looked at all the people.

"Are we going to have a party?"
he asked.

"We weren't," said his father.
"But we are now."

"Good!" said Frank.

"Yes," said Mrs. Early. "Everyone
must stay for supper."

Miss Green said, "I know you are not
ready to feed so many people. I'll go
to my shop and get ice cream."

Mr. Singer said, "I have a box
of balloons in my shop. I'll get
them for the party."

So they had a wonderful party.
Everyone ate and ate. John had
three helpings of ice cream and cake.
Sleeping had made him so hungry!

221

Magic Travel

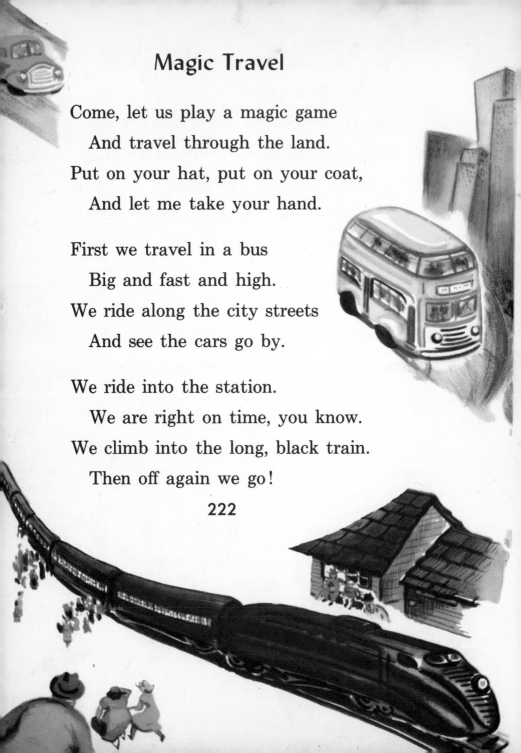

Come, let us play a magic game
　And travel through the land.
Put on your hat, put on your coat,
　And let me take your hand.

First we travel in a bus
　Big and fast and high.
We ride along the city streets
　And see the cars go by.

We ride into the station.
　We are right on time, you know.
We climb into the long, black train.
　Then off again we go!

222

We see a river and some boats
And up alone so high,
We see a big red airplane
Flying in the sky.

We travel on for hours
And all along the way,
We see a lot of places
Where we would like to stay.

When the evening puts a stop
To our magic play,
We find we had a lot of fun
But did not go away!

Handspring the Clown

The funny little clown felt sad.
"My name is Handspring, but I can't
turn handsprings," he said. "I am
only a picture clown. I must sit
in this shop until someone buys me."

A fat, happy-looking policeman
looked over the top of his box.

"Your hour will come,"
said the policeman. "People like us
must wait until we are needed."

"I wish someone would send me
away soon," said the little clown.
"I want to say hello to a little boy."

Just then a woman's hand reached down
and took the little clown.

A voice said, "Just what I want!
A picture of a clown to send
to Freddie Dresser! He will be
seven years old in the morning."

"Where does Freddie Dresser
live?" asked the shopkeeper.

"In Kingstown,"
answered the woman.
"That's a long way off."

"An airplane can get there
in five hours," said the shopkeeper.
"It is the fastest way to travel.
Send the little clown by airplane.
Then he will reach Kingstown
early in the morning."

"That's just what I'll do," said the woman.

"Good!" thought Handspring.

"I'm going on my travels at last!"

The woman gave the shopkeeper some money.

"Now I must write Freddie's name," she said.

"You may sit here and write,"
said the shopkeeper.

The woman sat down at a table.
She began to write Freddie's name,
street, and city.

"I hope Freddie likes this clown,"
she said as she left the shop.

"I can't think of any boy who doesn't
like clowns," said the shopkeeper.

"And Handspring is a good one!"

The woman walked
up the street.
She put Handspring
into a letter box.
He fell on top
of many other letters.

Handspring waited to see what would
happen. Soon a man opened the box
and put all the letters into a bag.
Then he took them to a large office.
There, workers looked
at each letter. They put the city letters
in one place. They put the out-of-town letters
on two tables. One table was for train letters.
The other was for airplane letters.

Handspring thought,
"Now what?"

227

Once again Handspring was crowded
into a bag. Now he was
with other airplane letters.

He heard a man's voice say,
"We must hurry! I hope this bag
reaches the field on time."

The bag was put into a truck, and
the letters rode to the landing field.

On the way the little clown talked
with the other letters.

"I am going to Kingstown," he said.

"I am going to a town called Hilltop,"
said a long yellow letter.

"I am going very far,"
said a pretty blue letter. "I must
hurry to White Cap City.
Then I'll travel on until I reach
another country far away."

In a short time the truck
reached the landing field.

The bag was put into the airplane,
and soon the airplane took off.
Up, up, up into the sky it went.

Handspring went to sleep.
He did not see the roofs
and chimneys far, far down.
He did not see the hills
and the rivers. He knew nothing
until the airplane landed at Kingstown.
Then he woke up with a jump.

"What happened?" he asked.

"We have landed," laughed his friends.
"This is Kingstown!"

229

A few hours after that
a man called at a little white house.

"Here is a letter for you, Freddie,"
said the man. "It came by airplane."

Freddie opened the letter.

"Oh!" he laughed. "This funny clown
came all the way from Garden City."

The man said, "What a story
he could tell you if he could talk!"

The funny little clown smiled.

"So I could," he thought.

"But Freddie can read what I have to say.

I am Handspring the clown
And I want you to know,
That I've come to town
Just to say hello
To a boy who is seven today."

A Busy River

Three children stood in the wheelhouse
of the River Girl. George and
Betty Long and Sonny Downs.
Sonny's father stood at the wheel
of the boat.

"We are almost there," said George.

The River Girl was just
coming into Garden City.
The children could see
rooftops and chimneys.
They could see the bridge.

231

After a short time, the boat reached
the landing.

Mr. Downs said, "The boat stops here
for a few hours. We can land, and
I'll show you some of the city."

"We have waited a long time
to see Garden City," said George.

"Where shall we go first?" Betty asked.

Mr. Downs smiled. "To see something
you have never seen before," he said.
"This city makes many things out of wood.
It's called the Woodwork City.
I'll take you to a workshop where
beds, chairs, and tables are made."

"How do we get there?" Sonny asked.

"We will take a bus," said Mr. Downs.

They rode down Kingman Street,
looking at the stores and buildings.

When they came to the workshops,
the busman let them off.

"Here we are," said Mr. Downs.
"Mr. Summers runs this shop.
Your father knows Mr. Summers."

"I've heard of him," said Betty.

They went into a large building
and found Mr. Summers in his office.

"How do you do?" said Mr. Downs.
"Here are George and Betty Long.
They would like to see your shop."

"You must be Frank Long's children,"
said Mr. Summers. "How do you like
your new home at River Farm?"

"It's wonderful," said Betty.
"But we like to travel, too."

"How long did it take you to reach
Garden City?" asked Mr. Summers.

"We went as far as Springfield
on Father's work boat," said George.
"That took us four hours."

"We stayed all night with Uncle Ted
in Springfield," his sister went on.
"Today Mr. Downs brought us
to the city on the River Girl.
That took almost five hours."

"And now you would like to see
whatever you can," said Mr. Summers.
"Come. I'll take you through the shop."

234

They went into a large room.
There they saw many men working
at wheels and saws.

"What makes the saws run?" asked George.

"Singing River helps to turn the wheels,"
answered Mr. Summers. "The wheels turn
the saws."

The children watched the wood being
made into beds, chairs, and tables.
Then some of the pieces were painted.

"Where do you get the wood?" Betty asked.

"It comes from far up the river,"
said Mr. Summers. "Almost all of it
is brought from Green Hills."

"Green Hills!" said Betty.
"Maybe Father's boat has helped
carry some of the wood here!"

"Yes, it has," said Mr. Summers.
"And now come here. Can you keep
a secret?"

"I like secrets," said Betty.

Mr. Summers showed them a chair
that was being put into a box.

"What a pretty chair!" said Betty.

"Read what's on the box,"
said Mr. Summers.

Betty began to read

MRS. FRANK LONG

RIVER FARM

GREEN HILLS

"Why, that's our mother!" said Betty.
"Does she know about this?"

"No," said Mr. Summers.
"But your father does. He asked us
to make it as a surprise for her.
The wood came from the trees
on River Farm."

"Our trees!" said Betty. "And now
they are coming back to us!
Thank you for telling us the secret."

Mr. Summers said, "We should thank
Singing River. It helps us in many ways."

"Yes," said Mr. Downs.
"It turns the wheels in our workshops,
and our boats sail on its waters."

"I like Singing River," said Betty.

What Do You Think?   Details

What is another name for Garden City?
Who is Mr. Summers?
What things for the home did the children see?
What secret do the children learn?
Where does the wood come from?

Study Pages

Vowel Sounds

Say each word and the sound of the vowel letter.

a in **at, sad, can't**

e in **get, send, step**

i in **it, think, fix**

o in **not, shop, rock**

u in **but, run, bus**

How many vowel letters do you see in each word?

Is the last letter in each word a vowel or a consonant?

The vowel sounds in **at, get, it, not,** and **but** are called short.

What words have short vowel sounds?

place	men	bill	use
king	glad	hope	smile
Frank	write	hot	felt

What word goes with **face**? With **hand**?

Other Vowel Sounds

Say each word and the sound of the
vowel in the word.

  a in **came**, **made**, **ate**
  i in **ride**, **write**, **five**
  o in **hope**, **nose**, **home**
  u in **use**

How many vowel letters do you see
in each word? Is the letter **e** heard
in each word?

The vowel sounds in **came**, **ride**, **hope**,
and **use** are called long.

What words have long vowel sounds?

I've	close	top	ice
send	face	smile	men
woke	fix	safe	place

What word goes with **snow**?
What word goes with **broken**?

Do You Know?

Have fun finding some of the answers.

Do cats live as long as rabbits?

How long do woodchucks live?

Do horses live as long as dogs?

Do people live as long as fish?

How Long Animals Live

Horses and rabbits eat plants.
But the horse may live for 25 years
and the rabbit, for five years.

Fish live on whatever they can find.
Some of them may live about 15 years.
Others may live as long as 60 years.

Cats and dogs eat many of the things
that people eat. Some of them live
as long as 15 years.

Vowels and Their Sounds

1. In **sad**, **send**, **it**, **not**, and **but**
the vowel sound is short. Each word
has only one vowel letter.

2. In **ate**, **like**, **home**, and **use** the
sound of the first vowel is long.
Each word has another vowel, the last
letter **e**, with no sound.

Say each word and its vowel sound.
Is it like **1**? Is it like **2**?

face	drive	rode	write
sun	fix	hot	bus

Here are four new words from the
next book. Look at each one. Is it
like **1**? Is it like **2**? Say the word.

side	rush	while	flash

Which new word could be used in place
of **hurry**?

PHONIC SKILLS
AND
THINKING ABILITIES

Two types of direct and practical help are given in this section (pp. 238-261) of this storybook:

1. Introduction to phonic skills needed for identifying the vocabulary of the selections
2. Introduction to thinking abilities required for the satisfactory comprehension of the selections

Purposes

These activities serve two purposes:

1. *New skills.* For teaching new skills when they are needed
2. *Self help.* As a source of self help for the pupil

The sequence for teaching new skills and reviewing them is detailed in *The ABC Teacher's Guide: Second Reader (2-1)*. In addition, specific suggestions for teaching new skills are given in both the teacher's guide and the teacher's edition of this storybook, providing the busy teacher with practical help at the right time.

Use

Activities in this section of the book are used after the first (silent) reading of a selection. About three to five minutes are required for each one.

The phonics-thinking pages at the end of each unit of this book are used to:

1. Teach new phonic-thinking skills
2. Review learnings
3. Help the pupil to apply skills to selected words from the next unit

For pupils who need additional help, these phonics-thinking pages may be used with one or more of the following:

Betts-Welch ABC Phonic Charts

Betts-Welch Study Book for *The ABC Down Singing River*

Pathways to Phonic Skills (recordings)

PHONIC SKILLS: AUTOMATIC USE

Children can be taught to use phonic skills and other word-learning skills automatically. When the use of these skills is automatic, pupils can then give their attention to the real purpose of reading: getting the thought.

Teaching New Skills

Teaching new phonic skills is done by having the pupils follow four easy steps:

1. Listen to the sound of the letter or syllable phonogram in the spoken word; e.g., the sound of *tch* \ ch \ in *catch,* of *o* \ ō \ in *home,* or of *er* \ -r \ in *farmer*

2. Say the vowel sound of the syllable

3. Identify the letters of the phonogram representing the sound or syllable

4. Check the use, or meaning, of the word in its sentence setting

Application of Skills

Teaching the application of phonic skills during silent reading-study activities is done by having the pupils:

1. Identify the unknown phonogram in the printed word

2. Recall the sound(s) represented by the phonogram

3. Identify the meaning of the word in its sentence

Specific suggestions for teaching the pupil to use his phonic skills automatically are given in the Teacher's Edition: Annotated and Keyed.

THINKING

In this storybook, the thinking and phonic activities are carefully interwoven. For example, the study of last syllables *y* and *er* and compound words contributes to the pupil's (1) correct usage of words and (2) phonic skills.

Introducing New Learnings

This development of new learnings is done by having the pupil follow two steps:

1. Relate the purpose of the activity to the selection in this storybook
2. Complete the activity and identify—when practical—similar situations in the selection

Application of Learnings

New learnings are applied by the pupil during his silent reading and in activities following the silent and/or rereading. Silent and oral rereading afford many opportunities to interpret punctuation, discuss shifts of meanings of words, and make other applications.

CHILD LEARNINGS

This basic reading-study program helps the pupil (1) to mature in his *interests,* (2) to make automatic use of *phonic* skills, and (3) to develop *concepts* and *thinking* abilities which insure comprehension. Detailed suggestions for achieving these goals are given in *The ABC Teacher's Guide: Second Reader (2-1).*

All previously taught skills are maintained in this book. (See Teacher's Edition: Annotated and Key.) New skills follow.

Phonics (letters and syllables)

1. Sounds of vowels with *r,* as *air*er*in *chair*

2. Vowel rules: single vowel, as *u* in *fun, e* in *went;* final *e,* as *u* in *use*
3. Vowel rules in stressed syllables, as *a*\a\ in *landing; e*\e\ in *clever, i*\i\in *sister, u*\ə\in *supper*
4. Consonant sounds, as *wh*\hw\ in *wheel, ng*\ng\ in *king, tch*\ch\in *catch, th*\th\in *their*
5. Syllable rule: *ed* is a separate syllable after words ending in *t* or *d,* as *wait—waited, need—needed*

Thinking

1. Language
   a. The syllables *er* and *est,* as in *faster* and *fastest*
   b. Contractions of *is* and *not,* as in *here's* and *didn't*
2. Definite and indefinite terms; e.g., *one week, nothing*
3. Classifying ideas, as *barn, house,* etc. are *buildings*
4. Suffix *y* as in *hilly*
5. Context clues: related ideas, classification, opposites
6. Idiomatic expressions; e.g., *look after*
7. Perception of relationships between ideas, as wheel—wagon, leg—?

First Sounds: **b, s, f, w** (See Teacher's Guide for use of this page.)

Pages 6–18   Pages 19–30   Pages 31–46

boat Betty town	be boat bus but	Betty bus tail boat
sing boat sail	sail sat some sing	sail sing say carry
rock fair fall	funny family fish fisherman	family men fire field
water week river	work woods wish wife	John wife warm woods

Rhymes: **ing, ay, y, en** (See Teacher's Guide for use of this page.)

| Pages 6–18 | Pages 19–30 | Pages 31–46 |

boat sing	sing king	king thing tail spring
stay an	hay way	day say through may
by ate	fly my	by why sky rocks
brought hen	when then	wife hen then men

fish	One day George was fishing
sing	in Singing River.
walk	Soon Betty came walking by.
catch	"Are you catching a fish?"
	Betty asked George.

Pages 19–30

sail	An old fisherman was sailing
look	his boat. He was looking
	for fish.
turn	Soon he was turning his boat
	around to go home.

Pages 31–46

say	"I am cold," the king was saying
	to his men.
carry	Soon the men were carrying wood
	to the fireplace.
warm	The king was warming his hands.

First Sounds: **cl, tr, ch, th** (See Teacher's Guide for use of this page.)

Pages 48–65   Pages 66–77   Pages 78–90

clock

noise

clothes

clothes

climb

clever

clever

clothes

drink

train

truck

seen

tree

travel

train

train

travel

smile

heard

children

chimney

chimney

children

change

change

cream

children

thank

wear

thought

thing

thought

thank

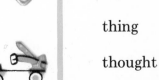

sky

thing

thought

241

thank   land

land   back

king   an

a in at

black

pat

fish

bag   left

met   best

left   men

e in egg

met

bat

yes

sing   king

spot   fill

fill   Dick

i in it

stop

drink

miss

get   rock

rock   not

box   spot

o in on

doll

John

let

242

Long and Short Sounds of i

Sometimes the letter **i** has a short sound, as in the word **is.**

Sometimes it has a long sound, as in **ice.** There is another vowel letter in the word **ice.** It is the last letter **e,** and it does not have a sound.

Find each word like **ice.** The long sound of **i** is heard, but the sound of **e** is not.

wife	smile	like	drink
pine	fill	prize	pie

Long and Short Sounds of a

Sometimes the letter **a** has a short sound, as in the word **at.**

Sometimes it has a long sound as in **ate.** There is another vowel letter in the word **ate.** It is the last letter **e,** and it does not have a sound.

Find each word like **ate.** The long sound of **a** is heard, but the sound of **e** is not.

safe	land	place	name
made	late	gave	bag

Words with **er**

Put **er** on the word **farm,** and you have **farmer.**
A farmer is a man who lives on a farm.

Find each word with **er.**

wait   A waiter may get you some milk.

paint   The painter paints the house.

sing   A singer likes to sing.

jump   The woodchuck is not a good jumper.

work   Everyone should be a good worker.

Long and Short Sounds of **e**

Sometimes the letter **e** has a short sound,
as in the word **get.**

Sometimes it has a long sound, as in **week.**

Find each word like **week.** The long sound
of **e** is heard, and two **e**'s are seen.

feed   need   left   three

feet   met   keep   seen

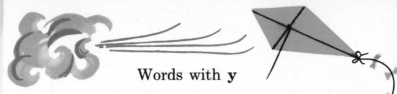

Words with **y**

Put **y** on the word **wind,** and you have **windy.**
It is a windy day when the wind blows.

Find each word with **y.**

rain   It was a cold rainy day.

hill   The country was hilly, and
            the children had fun climbing.

Other words have **y,** too, as **many, very.**

Find each word with the last part like **many.**

city	Mary	open	Betty
young	ready	story	carry

Words with **er**

Some words have **er** in the last part,
as **reader, keeper.**

Other words have **er** in the last part, too,
as **river, clever.**

Find each word with the last part **er,**
as in **river.**

after	paper	sister	alone
top	never	over	mother

You know many helps to new words.
Here are three of them. Read each one.
Then find the one you would use with
the new words that follow.

1. One vowel letter with a short sound,
   as in **milk** and **get.**
2. Two vowel letters, one with a long sound
   and an **e** with no sound, as in **ice.**
3. Rhymes, like **cold** and **hold.**

Use one help to say each new word.

drive   told   sit   leg

Here are three other helps for saying
new words. Read each one.

1. Two **e**'s, with a long **e** sound, as in **need.**
2. Last part with **y,** as in **only** and **Mary.**
3. Last part **er,** as in **Pepper.**

Use one help to say each new word.

sleep   supper   early   hurry

lion	sit	aunt
station	roof	plant
stood	foot	stand
leg	brook	gold
happen	took	thank
kitchen	sleep	think
been	read	land
top	top	found
seen	stood	went
travel	wait	field
tail	sad	told
goat	need	drink

247

Long and Short Sounds of i

The short sound of **i** is heard in **sit.**
The **i** is the only vowel letter in the word.
Use this help to say the following words:

think   milk   still   bill

The long sound of **i** is heard in **wife.**
There is another vowel letter in this word.
It is **e,** but it is not heard.
Use this help to say the following words:

ice   smile   drive   five

Long and Short Sounds of a

The short sound of **a** is heard in **sad.**
The **a** is the only vowel letter in the word.
Use this help to say the following words:

plant   an   sat   has

The long sound of **a** is heard in **safe.**
There is another vowel letter in this word.
It is **e,** but it is not heard.
Use this help to say the following words:

ate   place   face   cake

Long and Short Sounds of o

Sometimes the letter **o** has a short sound, as in the word **top.**

Sometimes it has a long sound, as in **home.** There is another vowel letter in the word **home.** It is the last letter **e,** with no sound.

Find each word like **home.** The long sound of **o** is heard, but the sound of **e** is not.

woke	rode	close	stop
hope	box	Joe	nose

Long and Short Sounds of e

Sometimes the letter **e** has a short sound, as in the word **pet.**

Sometimes it has a long sound, as in **keep.**

Find each word like **pet.** The short sound of **e** is heard, and only one **e** is seen.

men	sleep	fell	step
bed	leg	left	need

Here is a new word: **team.**

By looking at its letters and thinking
of words you know, you can learn to say it.
The word **team** has the first letter of **top.**
It has the last three letters of **cream.**

Now look at each new word that follows.
Find the two words that help you say
the new word.

New Word	Old Words		
seed	sit	cream	need
strong	street	cap	long
grew	step	grow	knew
glad	fell	glass	sad
hot	hold	not	bill
sun	sail	cake	fun

You know many helps to new words.
Here are three of them. Read each one.
Then find the help you need
with the new words that follow.
1. One vowel letter with a short sound,
   as in **sit, land, went.**
2. Last part with **y,** as in **Sonny.**
3. Rhymes, like **top** and **stop.**

Use one help to say each new word.

money   shop   fix   Frank   send

Here is another way that may help you.
New letters placed before an old word
sometimes make a new word. The letters **sm**
placed before **all** make the word **small.**
Use this help to find each new word.

Place **h** before **our.**   hot   hour   care
Place **r** before **each.**   reach   chair   team

First Sounds

paws
police
pet
large

Rhymes

stop
I've
shop

Words with **ing**

send	fixing
fix	sending
finish	dressing
dress	finishing
plant	thinking
think	planting

Vowel Sounds

pet	long **i**
sit	short **e**
write	long **e**
seed	short **i**
cap	long **o**
rode	short **a**

Words with **y**

rainy	money
hilly	hungry
rocky	summer
office	hurry

Words with **er**

painter	supper
worker	woodchuck
almost	winter
singer	answer

Are You Ready?

If you know the following, you are ready for the next book.

1. What short vowel sound is heard in each word?

   hot   glad   milk   left

2. What long vowel sound is heard in each word?

   write   place   seen   close

3. What vowel letter is not heard in each word?

   face   five   woke   cake

4. Say each word that has the same first sound.

   shall   think   short   shop

5. Say each word that has the same last sound.

   reach   found   send   land

6. Say each word that has the last part **er.**

   station   traveler   supper   paper

7. Say each word that has the last part **y.**

   early   hurry   police   city

8. Find the first letter and last part of this new word: **tall.**

   First letter: l   d   f   t

   Last part: one   all   our   aunt

Page 22   They sat down and ate their cookies.

Their cookies does not tell how many cookies the children ate.

So she put a cookie on the rock.

A cookie tells how many cookies Betty put on the rock. She put **one**.

Do you know how many?

Page 6	a house	Page 18	an old box
Page 9	the doors	Page 19	a big yellow bus
Page 16	some cookies	Page 21	a big black rock

Do you know how far?

Page 7	up the river	Page 21	into the woods
Page 17	a long way	Page 22	up the road

Do you know when?

Page 8	Soon	Page 19	When school was over
Page 12	One day		
Page 13	Next day	Page 19	now
Page 14	After a time	Page 22	When we were little
Page 16	Just then		

Pat <u>wasn't</u> in the kitchen.

Pat <u>was</u> <u>not</u> in the kitchen.

didn't

couldn't

there's

Jack's in the bus.

Jack is in the bus.

don't

what's

here's

Let's carry the basket.

Let us carry the basket.

isn't

hadn't

Hilly country has many hills.

Hill + y → Hilly

A rocky field has many __?__ .

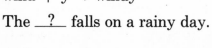

The wind blows on a windy day.

wind + y → windy

The __?__ falls on a rainy day.

Jack likes to go down
to the river to see the ____ .

There George saw a mother cat
and her two little ____ .

kittens
boats
dolls

Pat, Penny, and other ____
were going to a party.

Out of the black box came
a ball, a bat, and other ____ .

pictures
children
toys

"It's too cold," said George.
"I like to stay where it's ____ ."

On fair days and ____ days
the men work on the river.

rainy
safe
warm

"Can I help you?" Pat ____ .

"Maybe I can change his spots,"
____ Sue as she looked at Spot.

thought
asked
answered

head

tail

morning	evening
left	right
before	after

ask	answer
nothing	something
sad	happy

black	white
first	last
young	old

aunt	uncle
city	country
give	take

poor ____ ?   light ____ ?

king ____ ?   pull ____ ?

warm ____ ?   never ____ ?

257

The children took their places at the table.

Did the children pull off pieces of the table? No. They sat down and were ready to eat supper.

Let's play ball when the rain is over.

Once upon a time there was a poor king.

Uncle Freddie looked after the boys.

What do you want when you are hungry?

    sleep   supper   book

Who is your aunt?

    father's sister   father's mother

        sister's mother

What do you do when you hurry?

    sit   run   sing

What would a man drive?

    elevator   bus   boat

read —— book   wear —— clothes
You read a book.   You wear clothes.

eat —— cake   drink —— ?

drive —— bus   fly —— ?

foot —— leg   hand —— ?

wheel —— wagon   leg —— ?

left —— right   near —— ?

early —— late   morning — ?

pine —— tree   barn —— ?

lion —— animal   kitchen — ?

airplane   evening   milk

arm   far   room

building   present   table

All the buildings are high, but the
one at the right is the highest.

The blue train has five cars, and the
red train has two cars. The yellow one
has seven cars.

What is the color of the longest train?

Polly is seven years old, and her sister
Sue is five. A neighbor, Betty, is four
years old.

What is the name of the oldest girl?

Who is the youngest girl?

Farmer Green called his horses from the
field. On the way three brown horses went
to the brook for a drink. Whitey, an old
horse, walked. So young Blacky was first
to get to the barn.

What was the name of the fastest horse?

Neighbors: Mrs. Hope, Man, Woman, Mr. Jack

Things: Penny, Dress, Money, Clothes

Classifying Ideas
Pages 208-214

Bed, chair, and table are ____.

Coat, dress, and cap are ____.

Cake, pie, and candy are ____.

Red, green, and yellow are ____.

Summer, winter, and spring are ____.

School, house, and station are ____.

Woodchuck, rabbit, and bear are ____.

 Down Singing River

NEW WORDS: 183   CUMULATIVE VOCABULARY: 490

The ABC Down Singing River follows the series *The ABC On Our Way, The ABC Time to Play, The ABC All in a Day, The ABC Up the Street and Down,* and *The ABC Around Green Hills.*

The ABC Down Singing River and the accompanying study book introduce and develop the 183 words listed below.

A unique approach to phonic and thinking skills is given on pages 238-261 of this book. In addition, The ABC Phonic Charts and Pathways to Phonic Skills, Recordings, may be used for both group and individualized activities.

Specific suggestions for using this book and the accompanying study book are given in the Teacher's Guide.

The vocabulary chart below indicates the page on which each of the 183 new words is introduced in *The ABC Down Singing River*. All variants of a word, with the exception of those ending in *s, 's, s', d, ed, es, ing,* and *est,* are counted as new words. Contractions in which one letter is omitted are not counted as new words. In addition, exceptions are made for compounds of two known words and for words ending in the suffixes *y* and *er* (agent).

UNIT I	18. an	29. king	42. John
5. river	19. bus	30.	uncle
6. George	family	31. warm	43. . . . .
boat	20.	32. fire	44. sky
7. Betty	21. woods	place	through
8. sing	table	33.	45. . . . .
9. ate	22.	34. why	46. . . . .
10.	23.	35.	
11.	24. wife	36. tail	
12. answered	poor	37. say	UNIT II
13. brought	25. enough	thought	47. . . . .
along	fisherman	38.	48. aunt
14. rocks	26. use	39. fields	before
15.	give	40.	49. filling
16. sail	27. turned	41. carry	50. heard
17.	28.	men	noise

51. ice
52. . . . .
53. . . . .
54. kitchen
55. seen
    never
56. met
    wear
57. clothes
58. . . . .
59. . . . .
60. . . . .
61. land
62. . . . .
63. left
    been
64. buildings
65. . . . .
66. cream
    safe
67. clever
    nothing
68. . . . .
69. wagon
70. pulled
71. traveled
72. sister
    ball
73. change
74. magic
75. ever
    hurt
76. . . . .
77. . . . .
78. once
    goats
79. drink
    followed
80. room
81. until

82. . . . .
83. . . . .
84. . . . .
85. smile
    wait
86. evening
87. light
88. voice
89. . . . .
90. . . . .

UNIT III

91. . . . .
92. corn
    every
93. bark
94. watch
    foot
95. four
96. woodchuck
97. . . . .
98. . . . .
99. only
    learned
100. should
101. milk
    need
102. keep
103. sad
104. . . . .
105. city
    alone
106. young
    piece
107. paper
    read
108. . . . .
109. . . . .
110. . . . .

111. . . . .
112. floors
    neighbors
113. elevator
    top
114. opened
    Mary
115. roof
116. . . . .
117. . . . .
118. drive
    happened
119. told
120. sit
121. wonderful
122. . . . .
123. supper
124. ago
    any
125. station
126. sleep
127. early
    hurry
128. legs
129. . . . .
130. lion
    think
131. plants
    hungry
132. knew
133. . . . .
134. . . . .
135. found
136. . . . .
137. stood
    bridge
138. . . . .
139. pictures
140. . . . .
141. . . . .

142. . . . .

UNIT IV

143. . . . .
144. pet
145. five
    face
146. small
    still
147. bill
148. . . . .
149. . . . .
150. . . . .
151. Santa Claus
    Christmas
152. always
    winter
153. cake
    presents
154. . . . .
155. near
156. . . . .
157. . . . .
158. paws
159. close
160. woke
161. fell
162. rode
163. seven
    bed
164. secrets
165. hope
    cap
166. dressed
167. step
168. . . . .
169. . . . .
170. I'll
171. busy
    finish

172. team	UNIT V	202. office	221. . . . .
short	187.	203.	222. . . . .
173.	188. shop	204. I've	223. . . . .
174. strong	few	205.	224. . . . .
175. grew	189. fixed	206.	225. . . . .
seeds	chairs	207.	226. . . . .
176. crowds	190. hour	208.	227. . . . .
hot	191. Frank	209.	228. . . . .
177. glad	192. money	210.	229. . . . .
178. felt	193.	211.	230. . . . .
179.	194.	212.	231. . . . .
180.	195. reach	213.	232. . . . .
181.	196. send	214.	233. . . . .
182. summer	197.	215.	234. . . . .
183. sun	198. large	216. police	235. . . . .
can't	199.	217.	236. . . . .
184. care	200.	218.	237. . . . .
185.	201. almost	219.	
186.	writes	220.	

PHONICS–THINKING ACTIVITIES: Pages 238-261

ACKNOWLEDGMENTS

Grateful acknowledgment is made for permission to adapt and use the following copyrighted material:

"Where Was John?" from "Joe" by Elena Baker; from *Child Life Magazine,* Copyright 1950; used by permission of the publisher.

"The Sun Tree" from "The Sunshine Tree" in *Old Swedish Fairy Tales;* used by permission of The Hampton Publishing Company.

"Spot" from "Changing Spot" by Helen Crow and "Seesaw the Duck" from "The Duck Who Unlearned to Quack" by Robert L. Grimes; used by permission of the authors and *Jack and Jill* magazine.